TEAM PRACTICE
AND THE SPECIALIST

An Introduction to
Interdisciplinary Teamwork

TEAM PRACTICE AND THE SPECIALIST

An Introduction to Interdisciplinary Teamwork

By

JOHN J. HORWITZ, Ph.D.

Professor, School of Behavioral and Social Sciences
San Francisco State College
San Francisco, California

CHARLES C THOMAS • PUBLISHER

Springfield · Illinois · U.S.A.

Published and Distributed Throughout the World by

CHARLES C THOMAS • PUBLISHER

Bannerstone House

301-327 East Lawrence Avenue, Springfield, Illinois, U.S.A.

Natchez Plantation House

735 North Atlantic Boulevard, Fort Lauderdale, Florida, U.S.A.

*With THOMAS BOOKS careful attention is given to all details of
manufacturing and design. It is the Publisher's desire to present books that are
satisfactory as to their physical qualities and artistic possibilities and
appropriate for their particular use. THOMAS BOOKS will be true to those
laws of quality that assure a good name and good will.*

361
H789t

Printed in the United States of America

RJ-1

To
Adele
Eleanor
Gussie

CONTENTS

120144

TEAM PRACTICE
AND THE SPECIALIST

An Introduction to
Interdisciplinary Teamwork

Chapter I

THE IMPORTANCE OF TEAM PRACTICE

STUDENTS of the helping and healing professions
in the seventies will more and more find that practicing their art
means working on a small team and identifying people from very
different fields as colleagues. Psychologists are hitched up with
psychiatrists and social workers; specialists in physical medicine
"treat the whole man" alongside rehabilitation counselors,
occupational therapists and nurses; probation officers and judges
find themselves mapping out the week's tasks in conference with
mental health workers. Future pastors, future teachers, future
home economists, future administrators, future physical therapists
are all learning about the ins and outs of interdisciplinary team
process.

This book provides a broad overview of the common
characteristics of teams in a wide variety of service settings. It
helps the student professional to see how similar situations can
give rise to similar problems in very different kinds of
organizations. The beginner just finding his way asks the same
kinds of questions everywhere, even though in each place, for each
staff, the answers may be different.

Professionals who can work effectively day in and day out in
collaboration with colleagues from other fields are involved in
some of the most exciting creative projects in the professions.
Students well into their classroom studies in field instruction or in
an internship and graduating students considering practice
opportunities realize that this is so. They want to know why some
jobs can only be done well by a mixed group, how
interdisciplinary teams actually operate, and what it takes to get
along in that sort of setup.

Even larger numbers of people need help that, under today's
conditions of specialization, cannot really be provided by a single
expert or even a group competent in various branches of the same

3

calling. Those who need the coordinated, integrated or sequential services of workers in several different fields increasingly are turning to interdisciplinary (interprofessional) teams. They are turning towards practice settings where colleagues plan joint operations taking everyone's schedule into account, agencies where people consult with one another on a regular basis. Staff who are familiar with the distinctive expertise of the several professions and who recognize that there are tasks at which an associate may be more capable, are increasingly in demand. The growing need is for professional workers who can collaborate as a group because they understand each other's language. These are people who share common (or at least compatible) goals and have more or less the same ideas about how different services ought to be lined up or tied together.

Of course team organization, like any system devised by mere mortals, doesn't always work out as planned. The successive chapters of this book discuss the several dimensions of planning, explaining typical designs, and some of the problems that have been encountered in practice and some solutions. Attention is focussed throughout on the concerns of the individual worker, especially the beginner.

Experience has shown that it is unwise to presume that there is but one way to organize team operations, that each profession's role is always the same and that colleagues somehow automatically share a common view of the division of labor. While many basic professional values are held in common, differences in emphasis (as we shall see) are by no means rare. And when it comes to making decisions, patterns of participation vary widely; what is reflected here is the range of leadership styles and power structures which have evolved in many different kinds of institutions over a period of years.

Teams commonly operate as parts of the staff in complex organizations of considerable size. There are organizations, like hospitals, that include several kinds of practice teams. In other organizations, ·only some of the workers are in interdisciplinary teams; this would hold true for disability-assessment units in a state welfare department. Still another organizational pattern prevails in agencies where there are no staff members who are not on an interdisciplinary team; the practitioners in a child guidance clinic work in this kind of atmosphere. Clearly, his team's relationship to the overall organization, and that organization's control of finances, operating policies, etc., are matters of major concern to the practitioner.

Learning about teamwork means developing relationships with colleagues, understanding their standards and expectations and any demands the employing organization makes of its staff. But the worker is involved with his own profession as well, and will want to be guided by basic principles as he learned them at school and through his professional association. Any professional person who is an employee may someday find on-the-job demands in conflict (or seemingly in conflict) with his sense of professional ethics. Of course, situations of this sort arise daily in nonteam practice as well; but a part of coming to feel at home in the team process means, for each member, coming to a reconciliation of team objectives with those of his own profession.

The interdisciplinary team is a social invention of some importance; it is a way of providing more effective help to more people who need it. As a way of making a greater and more integrated range of services available, the interdisciplinary team may bring to a number of fields of practice changes as portentous as those that a generation ago accompanied the shift from the one-room schoolhouse to the consolidated school district.*

To ensure comprehensive care today, more and more professional people are involved in arrangements precluding the necessity of referrals, collateral involvements, shuttling people around town. Increasingly, the effort is to bring a range of specialized services under one roof and to make consultations among experts the standard operating procedure rather than an extraordinary expedient.

Of course, bringing together professionals from a number of disciplines cannot guarantee that they will in fact work together as a team. Offices may all be under one roof, yet the occupants of those offices are sometimes loathe to cross the hall. A service

---

*The newer schools pool resources so that offerings can include science specialists, language labs and guidance counselors; it is no longer expected that each teacher do the entire job on his own.

process may just not get going because one member of the team, unfortunately the one wielding ultimate authority, is hesitant or indecisive. A similar difficulty might be presented by one specific example: the rehabilitation of a juvenile delinquent may fail to get started simply because the mental health workers never really knew the judge who was depending upon them for advice and had never determined just which questions he was really expecting them to answer. Much has yet to be learned about the circumstances that make for team failure, but knowing where teams succeed can help clear the way. It is crucial, first of all, to be concerned about the desires and puzzlements of each individual person being helped: in one rehabilitation center, for example, a team was puzzled by one Negro patient's unusual reluctance to accustom himself to a new artificial limb — until one worker began to explore how that particular black man felt about going around with one leg pink. Numbers of teen-age girls in the nation's largest city were held to be wayward and deprived of their freedom, until stubborn and imaginative team inquiry disclosed that often the desire of selfish mothers for time to be with their own boyfriends impelled the teenager to get out of the house.

To understand interdisciplinary team practice it is also necessary to understand the practitioners — as professionals, but as people, too. On a particular team, a social worker who happens to be the only woman may question the tendency of some colleagues to expect her to "mother" her clients (after all, there will be some cases where she can play her part more effectively if she acts in a quite unmotherly fashion). Another team may find that an opportunity to do some adjunct teaching in an associated university best satisfies its psychologists' very human desire for the recognition that status brings.

The presentation of team practice that follows commences with an overall view of the setup in various types of interdisciplinary work groups, placing this newer organizational pattern in the perspective of a history of the professions. The focus is on the ways group structure and relationships help (or hinder) getting the job done. Half a dozen thumbnail sketches exemplifying the variety of approaches likely to be encountered, moving from one team setting to another, and the typical phases in a team's history are discussed.

The position of the individual worker next becomes the center of concern in an exposition of processes of role definition and role negotiation, quite commonly encountered when people with incomplete understanding of one another's skills must map out ways of sharing responsibility. Each person's own goals and ambitions, his character and background, his affiliations and allegiances all affect the place he'll find for himself in the team. Factors affecting intrateam relationships are examined, and a description of several leader-follower constellations follows.

Technology, work flow and tempo, communication and assessment techniques, procedures for control of intake and output; these constitute the matters next examined. Attention is turned to problems of the division of labor, and to the impact of diverse professional philosophies upon the ways colleagues can assist one another. Decision-making processes in team settings are described in some detail.

An explanation of the ways teams are necessarily implicated in budgeting and planning operations of their parent organizations follows. Examples of problems encountered and expedients devised in rehabilitation centers, child guidance clinics, courts, hospitals and welfare agencies may help guide the thinking neophyte and experienced worker alike, regardless of the type of program with which he may at the moment be involved.

The last theme developed in this exposition relates team practice to tradition in the professions, exploring the impact of the new style upon historic concepts of the nature of experts' contributions to the helping-healing process. The place of a team-practice interlude in career patterns of nurses, physicians, psychologists, social workers and therapists is discussed and some questions are raised concerning professional schools' preparation of students for interdisciplinary team practice.

This book has been prepared with experienced practitioners as well as students and recent graduates in mind. It deals with questions of material concern to everyone in the team regardless of particular setting, since the problems of structure and ways of work seem essentially the same for all. Details in the content and circumstances of interdisciplinary practice vary, and there will be different answers to the essential questions. But the questions that are pertinent to the situation are the same questions everywhere, and it is to formulating the questions that this book is addressed.

Chapter II

AN ORIENTATION TO THE INTERDISCIPLINARY TEAM

DURING the past generation, especially, leaders in the helping professions have demonstrated increasing concern about the compartmentalization of services into an ever-increasing number of specialized domains. New fields of expertise have been recognized, and there has been a continuing effort to organize practice in such a way that each worker can spend the larger proportion of his time at tasks demanding substantive rather than merely incidental skills. But at the same time the need for serving the whole man has been reemphasized, and group practice designs which stress routine consultation and referral are taking the place of work settings in which each professional person can be a little king in his own domain. While interdisciplinary teamwork is not unknown in private practice, most teams are found in large, bureaucratically structured settings, where practitioners are paid employees; but those they serve can count upon the pooled skills of a number of specialists acting in concert.

When a group of workers come together to accomplish something none can manage on his own, more than a large aggregate of man-hours is involved. The common enterprise requires performance of specific tasks at which people in one field may be more accomplished than those in another. The workers may set up their own team or they may be brought together by an organization (like a health center or a juvenile court) that specializes in the provision of coordinated services. In any case, positions are commonly defined with reference to the expertness attributed to practitioners in various fields.

Each team member comes to the job endowed with specific authority by his own professional group: by virtue of some particular preparation, his ability to perform a range of

8

"appropriate" tasks is endorsed by generally recognized people in his own field.*

Professional people are expected not only to possess specific skills, but to know also what they are unable to do, what a more expert colleague should be asked to undertake. All this suggests that there are generally recognized boundaries identifying the circle of competence within which all workers identified by the same job title may practice. The fact is, however, that overlap is almost a commonplace in interdisciplinary team operations.

It is true that along with the development of professional expertness, there has been an increase in the measure of autonomy accorded workers in professional occupations. But in contemporary Western society, the rapid increase of scientific knowledge has provided more resources than any one specialist can hope to master. One result has been a trend toward delimiting areas of individual responsibility and increasing the proportion of professional work performed in collaborative processes articulating the segmental skills of different persons. In the helping professions — medicine (e.g., psychiatry), social work, clinical psychology — this trend has led to a proliferation of technical and subprofessional occupations. It has also led to the development of larger numbers of increasingly complex organizations, which in turn have created a trend toward the institutionalization of interdisciplinary team practice.

Interdisciplinary team practice seems to be organized in settings where personnel of a single discipline have perceived a need for certain services they themselves lack the skill to provide. Visiting teachers' (school social workers) involvement in public education and medical social workers' appearance in hospitals, for example, fill this need. Historically, another way interdisciplinary teams have come to be created is in response to pressure from society when certain problems are found to extend beyond the area of competence of a single discipline. The standardized triad of the psychiatrist, psychologist and social worker in child guidance would be an example in point, and also the multidisciplinary staffing in rehabilitation centers.

---

*Sometimes the government certifies or licenses him; but here too, assessment is by examiners who must in the last analysis be acceptable to those already in the field.

Occupations frequently involved in interdisciplinary teams are those of health educator, judge, nurse, occupational therapist, physician, physical therapist, probation officer, prosthetist, psychologist, recreationist, rehabilitation counsellor, social worker and speech therapist. Workers in additional occupations, such as clergymen and teachers, occasionally are involved as consultants. Since we have not made a point of rigorously distinguishing professional from nonprofessional workers, it should be noted that, in some settings, orderlies, cottage parents and "aides" of various sorts also participate in team conferences — regularly or by frequent special invitation. Alongside the well-established nonprofessional occupations, in recent years there has been a growing emphasis upon new categories of jobs especially designed to be filled by people drawn from the very population the team serves. In programs emphasizing departures from a "doing for" philosophy, there is a growing recognition of unique potentials in helping people to help themselves. Where those served are seen as a population rather than a series of unique cases, it may be argued that indigenous workers (conceivably people who themselves need or needed help) can provide the team very special insight and entree.

The Nature of Interdisciplinary Team Practice: An Introduction

At the heart of the concept of interdisciplinary teamwork is the joining of essentially dissimilar skills which colleagues in diverse occupations bring to bear upon different aspects of a common problem. In successful team practice, relationships that cross disciplinary boundaries may be the closest, and each practitioner is concerned with facilitating the achievement of all of his fellows. Smooth communication bridges the gaps between one worker's thinking and the useful ideas of his colleagues, and professional jargon is not cultivated as a conversational hurdle. Imaginative and fluid organizational routines are necessary to expedite work flow, even in practice situations where every single individual is unquestionably committed to a pooling of expertise.

A number of studies of team practice are agreed upon certain worker characteristics thought to ensure team solidarity. These include attitudes toward the work itself, such as dedication to a common ideal or working on a common problem, willingness to share the client, a professionally receptive outlook, flexibility, willingness to learn and willingness to accept decisions by consensus. Certain attitudes toward colleagues are also stressed: respect for colleagues — which implies a nonparochial outlook, confidence in colleagues' good will and confidence in colleagues' competence. Among the personal qualities frequently mentioned are: personality of the outreaching type, high-level communication skills and willingness to employ them, professional self-respect, self-confidence and personal professional competence. About other matters there is considerable difference of opinion. Some items are absent from many lists, e.g., the necessity for an effective leader or, for that matter, the necessity for any leader at all. There is room for debate as to whether group agreement on role definitions is a prerequisite to effective team practice. And whatever the compatabilities may be, there can be no denying that the values and ideals people in any particular profession hold in common are simply not identical with those of all others.

Therapeutic teams committed to the ideology of "total institutions" may forget that under ordinary circumstances those they serve lead segmented lives, ensuring themselves a measure of privacy by making home and occupation worlds apart or relating to one group of people in their leisure hours, another in their pursuit of civic interests. In a residential treatment setting describing itself in mental health terminology as a "therapeutic community," staff may think of a patient in the hospital laundry as involved in "industrial therapy," a patient playing the piano as involved in "recreation therapy." A practitioner who identifys the one as "work" and the other as "creative expression" might seem ideologically, not quite a member of the team.

A similar mystique often prevails with reference to records and reports. Each team evolves an informal code stipulating which conferences and discussions are charted or reduced to writing and which ones officially escape formal notice. There are exchanges which are very much a part of the history of an organization, a work group or a case which nonetheless are never recognized to have occurred at all. Practitioners may be under the impression that they are meticulously recording each consequential decision or exchange of opinions, yet the crucial turn of events may follow an informal consultation during the coffee break and never get into the minutes of a regular staff meeting.

There is a rough and ready practicality about work on a team in a service setting. This kind of practice puts to the acid test any blue-sky illusions of independence which may be brought to the job by a recent professional school graduate. The workers' on-the-job activities are expected to be compatible with organizational designs in team and agency. Discretion and judgment on the job are necessarily confined within limits set by the employer and the work situation. The latitude that team and complex organization allow the individual professional, however, varies greatly. Furthermore, in a particular setting at a particular time, great discretion in the employment of professional judgment may be allowed in therapy, for example, even though latitude in the selection of clientele, say, may approximate zero — or vice versa.

By and large, a team's preeminent goal is maximum service to those being helped, and this is the yardstick against which other values tend to be measured. Thus, sharing of power and a democratization of relationships among co-workers may be advocated, but if in a particular operating setting a convincing argument can be made that a hierarchical structure ensures more effective performance, that is the structure likeliest to be instituted. Authority may be shared to a degree, but the decision-making power commonly is more or less concentrated either by traditional authority (as in the license reserved to physicians in prescribing medication) or by limited privilege conferred by some larger organization within which the team practices. "Consent of the governed" (whether workers or recipients of service) is the exception, not the rule.

The Team in Developmental Perspective

The structure of an interdisciplinary team is itself the product of social, therefore historical, processes. The variety of patterns which may be observed have been evolved out of the interplay of traditions within institutions and agencies as well as the diverse ideologies and ways of work of various professions. Each team is also affected by social forces of a more unique character, e.g., the crosscurrents of power within a particular community in which the team works or will work. Structurally, one team may be a pyramid, its members sorted by professions into successive levels, with a chief from some traditionally authoritative discipline at the top; another may be a clearly defined discussion circle with no senior person. Not uncommonly, however, the setup changes as relationships within a group evolve over a period of time: the way the work actually gets done may prove on close examination to be rather different from the processes outlined in a table of organization. Furthermore, experience may suggest the need for adding a person with indispensable work skills not originally specified; or it may suggest that particular services need not in fact be provided by the team, as they are readily available collaterally in the community. Changes in personnel frequently eventuate in structural changes, since in interprofessional practice there may be a greater likelihood that the worker will change the position rather than vice versa.

For example, two teams in different settings may employ two members of a particular profession who have substantially similar expertness. But the two jobs, carrying identical position titles, are likely to have notably different operational demands, even though they both clearly require a number of identical occupational skills. Or two workers in the same profession employed on teams in similar settings may find their jobs differ materially because of distinctive factors in the histories of the larger organization, the team or particular colleagues with whom they work. It is no exaggeration to state that the character of team practice is so variegated, the strength of tradition so tenuous, that the same work unit in the same organization, engaged in the same practice, with no material alteration of goals, may change markedly from one year to the next. The team may change its shape like an amoeba, different members coming to the fore over a period of time; the shape of the team may actually vary at any given moment according to the particular pattern of work relationships judged to be most appropriate to the demands of particular practice situations and the needs of particular persons being helped.

Discussions of interdisciplinary team organization and structure rarely detail the successive steps involved in getting team members together before the team exists as an entity, but successive "phasing-in" periods are observable as a team is activized and begins to take on work. Occasionally, a group which has undertaken a short-term project may move to make the association permanent, endeavoring in the process to find in some complex organization a new home where they can work together. But more commonly, it is either an agency which decides to provide a service for which an interdisciplinary team is organized, or a key professional in any agency who decides his work needs the support he believes a team can provide.

It is quite common to encounter workers who take much pride in the fact that they have served with the team for as long as it has existed or, alternatively, that their period of work or service coincides with that of a new leader whose appearance marked the abandonment of an approach now identified as less effective. However, the processes in which it is possible to trace a developing team spirit remain essentially obscure. Most reports of team operations are cross-sectional in approach, and discussions of historical change that have been published are for the most part devoted to observations covering periods of only a few weeks or months.

The addition of personnel involved in the introduction of a new discipline to a team constellation will usually be preceded by exploratory discussions involving personnel in each of the other disciplines — in the case of the sizeable teams, perhaps senior personnel only. In complex organizations of considerable size, recruiting for teams may be a responsibility of senior personnel in the several disciplines who will work alongside the new team, including those who may be at a higher echelon than the new team's leader. Protocol relating to clearance with the team and especially with its leader, may be hotly debated. Not uncommonly, one party may initiate and screen hires while the other approves, either reviewing suggested candidates rigorously or reserving a largely ceremonial, *pro forma* right to reject.

Team effectiveness and, possibly, team survival are intimately related to the groups' developing its own characteristic ways of working together, and this typically is a continuing process, often on a trial-and-error basis. A spirit of group solidarity, also, is a factor in what might be described as the maturation of a group; if factionalism becomes characteristic of its inner life, the team has a problem to solve. Changes in the practice milieu, changes in the host agency and changes in service technique — all these present problems, and the group can grow while solving them. Solving them may raise both practice and group cohesion to new heights, but conflict can also eventuate in an epidemic lowering of morale and, conceivably, in the ultimate collapse of the enterprise.

Failure of a team to survive most frequently revolves about such factors as: (1) change in goal on the part of the complex organization serving as "host," or a shift in goal priorities there; "lack of funds" may be given as the explanation; in such an event; (2) one or another sort of "fall from favor," and consequent loss of power on the part of the team leader or a strategically-situated team member; or, alternatively, the fall from power of an individual in the complex organization with whom the team was in some critical fashion personally connected; (3) disputation within the team around interprofessional issues which proved disruptive, demoralizing and without significant outcome; or, alternatively, and perhaps most commonly, a combination of the three.*

Role Definition and Role Negotiation

Roles in an interdisciplinary team can be related only in the broadest outline to activities and relationships typical of one or another profession in some other operational context. Role relationships in interdisciplinary teams are characteristically the outcome of a more or less spirited and protracted bargaining process.

In an employment setting, a worker must anticipate a settling-in stage in which he discovers (usually over a period of time) just

---

*Although conflict is listed as a possible antecedent of a team's demise, this is not to say that it will always, or even most frequently, prove deleterious; a team may, in fact, be strengthened through a process of conflict resolution.

exactly what is expected of him and what he can reliably expect of others. In interdisciplinary team practice, the newcomer commonly finds that his job is rather undefined and that his colleagues have differing conceptions of the division of labor and the part he should play. Each member of the group sizes up the situation and indicates (explicitly or by implication) what he believes he can and should do, among the things he determines must be done. Obviously, co-workers differ in their perception of relevance of their own skills to the demands of a situation. It is equally obvious that there will be differences of opinion as to what needs to be done first and who should do it. Team operations almost invariably engender a continuing process of role clarification and redefinition, as colleagues debate the desirability of one or another worker performing particular responsibilities, exercising particular authority. In the give-and-take of everyday practice, a fair amount of negotiation seems necessary; no matter what memoranda may stipulate as to the way things work, in the field human beings filling one or another position size up the situation and strike a working bargain with the people they encounter as collaborators.

A clinical psychologist, for example, joining an interdisciplinary team may find that he is expected to know how to administer and interpret standardized tests and how to decide which instrument(s) are appropriate to the assessment of particular situations encountered in practice. A social worker may find he is expected to have a good working knowledge of personality development but that his colleagues think of him as primarily expert in interviewing techniques and in the location of extramural resources. Yet it is eminently likely that the two practitioners and their respective professional associations describe the work they are prepared to do with emphases on a somewhat different group of skills and capacities. And the workers are likely to find it necessary that they personally exercise some initiative in clarifying their appropriate contributions in this particular situation, regardless of the part played by others in that role definition process.

Not uncommonly, colleagues will endeavor to get the feel of a team and its situation without any planful determination to become involved in role bargaining. Nonetheless, an intricate series of inquiries and overtures is the common prelude to agreement on task performance obligations. Individual idiosyncracies and historical accident result in elements of job performance becoming traditionally attached to specified positions on a team.* Workers come to employment prepared in very different ways, and neither their professional experience nor their educations necessarily ensure a congruence of expectations and a common sense of reciprocal obligations.

In cases of disagreements about role definitions, the role-occupant, if in inferior status, may be faced with the classic dilemma — to accommodate to an objectionable reality or to try to change it. Clearly, each person must determine for himself the extent to which matters of high principle are involved in job considerations he finds questionable. Even where his concerns seem pressing, the worker will have to assess the tractability of the situation — the extent to which it is likely others may be persuaded to share his judgment of what is right and proper.

Confusions about role definition and the resultant debate, even recrimination, cannot be regarded as unusual in interdisciplinary team practice settings. It would seem that clarifying role expectations by discussion based upon careful analysis is therefore almost a necessity if group norms are to be developed. The appropriateness of particular activities to the professional mission of team members identified as specialists of one or another type is frequently a disputed point. What is not only acceptable, but expected and necessary for workers in one kind of organization to engage in, may be questioned or forbidden in another. Furthermore, practice may differ substantially even among agencies of the very same type. In one juvenile court, for example, a clinical psychologist may be employed solely to contribute to diagnostic assessment, while in another, a colleague identified with the same discipline is expected to render psychotherapeutic services as well.

---

*A principal, for example, took particular satisfaction in progressively more elaborate graphics and statistical charts prepared by the school social worker. When that practitioner retired, her replacement found herself confronted by demands of a rather unusual character, an on-the-job tradition of social work practice for which she had not been prepared.

Staff, under such circumstances, understandably may find their work situation a challenge to the creative imagination. Not uncommonly, role definition moves from one ostensibly *ad hoc* decision to another, as the team (or its captain) threads a way through the labyrinth of day-to-day practice. In some settings, the decisions about activities and responsibilities must be made independently by each discipline; decisions are eventually integrated with whatever other formulations have become more or less accepted.

Leadership

The personality characteristics "necessary" in a leader have been studied, though no systematic effort has been made to ascertain whether leaders of interdisciplinary teams as a class differ from the kind of people who lead other groups effectively. It is clear, nonetheless, that being imaginative and decisive is insufficient; a measure of status, organizationally conferred, is likewise needed if a leader is to be able to affect a team's operations materially.

But leadership essentially involves something more than status or a title, and the leader of a team is not merely a person possessed of certain traits or characteristics. Leadership in team practice situations involves facilitating the achievement of common goals. The leader is able to lead because of the working relationship that exists among a group of colleagues committed in principle to some over-arching professional purposes: conceptions of human needs to be filled, of human distress they can allay. As problematic incidents arise and issues want clarification from time to time, it becomes clear that the leadership of a team is lodged in the person or persons who can effectively influence the activity of others as they strive to achieve group goals. The personal influence leaders can exert, in turn, is affected by the structure of opportunity and responsibility defined by the larger organization that constitutes the group's work setting.

In formal organizations, the leader's span of control is established by some higher authority which is responsible for designating him bureaucratically and for supporting his power over those whom he leads. But interdisciplinary teams, even when articulated into complex bureaucracies, commonly retain some of the characteristics of an informal group, a colleague's status being in some wise dependent upon the tenor of his direct exchanges with other team members. The supervisor may extend his influence beyond the limits of his formal authority by the exercise of personal indulgence; this is no novelty in interdisciplinary team practice. The administratively senior person's power may be under continuous attack from colleagues who make autonomy a sacred professional value, and there may be continual negotiation for the "right" to procure office supplies without going through the requisitioning routine, etc.

In some groups, a single individual holds titular leadership, in others the status may not be formalized. But in any event, actual leadership will be found to be rotated if the activity of every member is observed and note is taken of the occasions when each influences the others. Upon occasion, every single team member initiates some activity or other in which colleagues join, and succeeds even fleetingly in inducing the others to follow. Some in a group lead only rarely and it may be that their leadership is not even perceived by colleagues. Conversely, recognized leaders do not lead all the time, do not provide all the leadership and are themselves followers upon occasion.

In many teams, leadership devolves upon the individual whose profession dominates the organization under whose auspices the group practices. Members of a profession dominant in an organization may take it for granted that in the event of differences of opinion, team decisions will be made by one of their own people. They may regard members of other disciplines as essentially ancillary. And practitioners from other fields may quite clearly voice their own sense of marginality in the setting; social workers, for example, refer to a hospital as a "host" agency. By the same token, workers who have earned doctoral degrees but are not physicians, may come into collision with medical colleagues because of competitive claims to the identical honorific title. In one hospital, for example, a clinical psychologist became embroiled in conflict because he insisted on being called "doctor."

Where a leader's influence is primarily attributable to

"charisma," it is because his colleagues believe that he has some remarkable personal quality — in a mental health team, for example, prodigious insight. The leader's charismatic authority will be freely wielded as long as this belief of his colleagues persists. If his "insight" impresses objective analysts as being no less fallible than his colleagues', his charisma is unimpaired as long as his teammates continue to harbor a contrary impression. Charismatic leadership, however, requires not only followers imbued by faith, but a practice setting whose structure permits such leadership to be exercised. Some individuals may be personally more disposed to invest a team leader with charismatic authority. And much of his authority may therefore depend upon the continued presence of particular personality types among colleagues in subordinate status.*

Yet leadership is frequently exercised by people who are not in any way striking "personalities." There is another component. Perhaps leadership is best thought of as a "function" rather than a status or position.

The leadership function commonly includes helping and teaching, allocation of work, and evaluation of performance. But it should be noted that any process of influence may be construed as a sort of leadership. In one hospital, for example, nursing aides on the wards were forbidden to make certain decisions or to use their own judgment in proscribed areas. But in practice, the green physicians actually responsible for patients were told by the aides what recommendations they believed desirable in the light of their own bedside experience. In nine cases out of ten, judgments based on empirical experience alone proved superior to those based on book learning, made by the higher status workers. While leadership by nonprofessionals is uncommon, there can be no denying the fact that there are occasions when they do show the way to higher status workers. The same may be said of nurses influencing doctors while ostensibly recognizing and deferring to their authority: their behavior may be properly respectful, "oriented" to a hierarchical establishment without necessarily "conforming"

---

*It is the followers willingness and desire to believe, of course, not the leader's attributes as such that support the charismatic relationship.

to its prescriptions. A nurse not contesting the doctors' status may upon occasion try to lead them, nonetheless.

Team practice tends to involve workers in certain characteristic social situations. Competition, perhaps attributable more to the work setting than to personality, is the keynote of one such "social drama." Aspects of team structure and process which may engender competitiveness may be divided into those arising out of task performance itself, and those pertaining to social relationships not necessarily technological. The satisfactions derived from saving a colleague, especially a powerful one, from the consequences of his own mistakes might fall into either category.

Specific work practices that apparently engender competition, often reflect the overlapping skills and responsibilities, especially among different disciplines. If persons assisted by the team are initially interviewed by but one worker, this intake process may be invested with special glamor. If persons of more than one discipline regard themselves as qualified to do this work, they may become competitive. Likewise, where several workers successively or simultaneously serve the same person, they may compete with one another for his affection; such competition may be criticized as a disruption of "transference" relationships. Of course, the person "served" may in fact be not a client but the team leader, and the transferences in this instance are theoretically not job-essential. Competition for the leader's affection, esteem or regard, is fairly common in team practice, and the competitive worker — or the leader who cultivates a competitive atmosphere — affects the unity of the entire group.

Contrariwise, team members may be reluctant to risk assuming a competitive stance. Their work style may revolve about repetition of the leader's observations or conclusions, or a scrupulous attempt to parallel the leader's clinical findings with reports of analogous data from the perspective of different expertness.

Just as intrateam competition may threaten solidarity, another special situation that may cause strain is the entry of a new worker into the team. No matter what constellation of relationships may previously have been worked out, the newcomer tends to throw existing arrangements into question, precipitating a reexamination, if not a revision, of the *de facto* table of organization. Furthermore, the decision to hire may itself be tied in with the internal "politics" of the group.

Like most initiation procedures, the introduction of the newcomer is potentially a threat to the integrity and personal dignity of those whose status has presumably already been established. Orientation must somehow be accomplished without doing violence to the new worker's own learning process. He is expected to act-through team-useful decisions. But if the process of becoming a part of the team culture is so accelerated that bone-and-marrow learning is disrupted, there will be a stultification of the new colleague's creative ingenuity — of those personal qualities which lie at the heart of professional functioning.

Not uncommonly the newcomer may be a beginner, just starting professional practice. He then undergoes "rites of passage" thrice over: as a neophyte in his calling, in this setting, and in team practice. Alternatively, the new worker may be experienced in his profession but not in team practice. Or he may be new only to the particular team, though experienced in his calling and in team practice settings.

Still another special situation is that of the worker cast as a scapegoat or a misfit. The person who doesn't fit into a team may be one who would not fit into any team, or simply an individual who could participate effectively in some other team, possibly many others. Incompatability of worker and team, in short, may arise out of characteristics of either, and a worker who doesn't fit into a particular team is not necessarily a misfit because of personal characteristics that are indisputably occupationally relevant. Lack of job-relevant skills is certainly one possibility, but it may be that latent qualities (age, sex, ethnicity) or "personality" may make for friction.

Six Teams in Miniature

The brief descriptive sketches of several typical but imaginary interdisciplinary teams that follow derive from our own observations in the field over a period of more than two decades and draw also upon published descriptions of interdisciplinary teamwork and reports of our students. The groups presented below exemplify many of the phenomena examined at greater length in the chapters that follow. These bird's-eye views should help orient the reader to the diversity of auspices, operations and personnel that characterize interdisciplinary team practice. Our endeavor at this point is merely to provide the reader a glimpse of the breadth of the field, and an idea of the kinds of variables found interacting in interdisciplinary team practice situations. These team portraits are designed to bring into coherent focus the principal elements of interdisciplinary teamwork, providing the reader with background against which he may view the diversity of more fragmentary illustrations throughout the text.

As an initial orientation to interdisciplinary team structure and process, we present below a view of two teams, not from a substantive perspective, but in organizational terms. Like the teams described toward the end of the chapter, any interdisciplinary team in any setting has an inner life: workers in various positions are interrelated by job and personal characteristics in one way or another so that they accomplish the team's missions – or subvert and disrupt the team's solidarity. The typology that follows sketches two very different patterns of relationship among colleagues. The content of the work has deliberately been omitted here, so that the reader may focus upon form.

A Leader-centered Team

Our first example is of a team which is a smooth-running ensemble whose members center their efforts on behalf of clients about the figure and decisions of a leader. His authority stems from his followers' faith in his strong personality (charisma) and he is sustained by the larger organization as well as by deference traditionally shown his profession. While status differentials exist and there is a certain amount of jockeying for prestige, competition among the other members is not of any consequence – the very possibility of competitiveness scarcely figures in the development of plans for group enterprises. Practice routines in the bureaucratic manner are emphasized; each person has his own job to do and tends to go about it on his own. Division of labor and the flow of work is as the leader decides, and he handles overlap problems in amiably received *ad hoc* decisions. Other members accept without substantial question his clinical judgment, the superiority of his pervasive expertness, his personal good will and his competence to evaluate their work.

Conversation is businesslike and at the minimum level compatible with good feeling among colleagues; the oral communications, like those in writing, are largely to and from the leader. The team relates to the complex organization through its leader and responds with passive resistance to "outside" efforts to develop liaison with other members if the leader disapproves. Members' concern with the views and standards of their respective professional associations (reference group behavior) tends to have rather marginal influence on the ongoing life of the team. Recruiting and indoctrination of new personnel perpetuates the pattern, and rebels or oddballs are dispensed with in short order. The whole team's stability is dependent upon continuities in the leader's behavior and in his own profession's status in the field. In the event of a break between his leader and personnel at superior echelons in the complex organization, however, he may seek another setting and be able to bring along his entire team, or all those acceptable in the new locale.

A Fraternally Oriented Team

Our second team is a fraternity of experts, amiably dividing the work by consensual decisions. Colleagues recognize the preeminence of one or another member's expertness with particular kinds of clients or in particular situations. Senior responsibility may pass in rotation to each specialist at a mutually recognized state of the work process. There is appreciation of differentials in skills coupled with a common acceptance of overlap as a fact of life, and team members value a continuing system of clinical consultation and mutual aid. Productive processes are flexibly organized, but tasks performed by individual workers are intimately integrated with those undertaken by others; there is little compartmentalization.

Work is allocated and divided, and new people are added to the group by common decision. Communication is oral for the most part, and those colleagues who have the most to say are simply the people who tend to be voluble whenever and wherever their contacts are unrestrained. The team's engagement with the complex organization is through a quasi-clerical worker for administrative procedures; where substantial professional concerns seem to the team to be at stake, each professional in turn "takes over," *ad hoc.* The group most commonly is short-lived, more so than the leader-centered team, and it is unlikely to move from setting to setting as a unit. Leadership, like other status differences, is played down.

After this glimpse of two typical approaches to organizing structure and process in interdisciplinary teamwork, we proceed to sketches of work groups as they operate in three different kinds of agency setting. In a space of the few pages immediately below, we have tried to introduce the reader to the distinctive character of service operations — what distinguishes one helping-healing field from another. Some of the themes epitomized in the illustrations above recur in the interdisciplinary teams we describe next. These same themes will continue to be developed from chapter to chapter as we piece together a comprehensive picture of interdisciplinary team practice. The brief descriptions of work relationships in a clinic, a court and a hospital which follow should add to the reader's understanding of uniformities as well as diversities in some newer approaches to professional team practice.

A Child Guidance Clinic Team

A child guidance clinic team typically includes a psychiatrist, a psychologist and a social worker; not infrequently there is more than one social worker, and sometimes more than one psychologist. The psychiatrist commonly is the clinical director and a troubleshooter therapist; he is ultimately responsible for certifying diagnoses and "closing" cases. Frequently he is the administrative director as well. The psychologist, originally brought into this setting as psychometrician, today commonly is engaged in psychotherapy as well as in the administration and interpretation of standard diagnostic instruments. The social worker, whose responsibility in the first post-World War I clinics was adjunctive therapy (counselling with parents), today generally works with children, too. A very large proportion of social workers, as well as many psychologists and psychiatrists in child guidance clinic teams, have had extensive field experience in interdisciplinary collaboration as part of their basic professional education. Integrated methods of practice come as no surprise.

A professional in any discipline may employ group or one-to-one technique in therapy, may treat only one member of a family or several members all together, seriatim or concurrently; therapy sessions with adolescents may be the "talking cure," but with young children play therapy is the technique frequently employed. Just as group techniques have been found both more expeditious and more effective in the treatment of certain adult personality disorders, so have child guidance teams brought together several clients, sometimes with more than one worker, in psychodrama or play therapy and also for diagnostic purposes.

Among the behavior disorders of children which are likely to be treated by child guidance clinics are: socially unacceptable manifestations of sibling rivalry, fire-setting, petty thievery diagnosed as compulsive, bed-wetting, socially objectionable behavior (e.g., bullying or rebelliousness) and crippling fears. Clinic caseloads also frequently include youngsters diagnosed not only as "clearly neurotic," but frequently "prepsychotic," as well as children diagnosed as actually psychotic (e.g., autistic or schizophrenic). Some teams limit their practice to such cases. Acceptance of a case in a child guidance clinic implicitly characterizes it as one in which problematic or deviant behavior in a youngster is presumed to be based on a personality or characterological problem. And the problem is assumed to have some roots in the behavior of a child's parents towards him, or toward one another; hence, the parents are regarded as secondary patients when the clinic accepts a child as patient, or the whole program may be explicitly identified as family-oriented.

Commonly, an evaluation of the dynamics of the child's problematic behavior is arrived at by personnel of all three disciplines. In conferences, they pool data and draw inferences from information received from the child's familial, school and even neighborhood setting; from his performance on various standardized psychological tests; and from his own behavior at the clinic in interview or play therapy. A therapeutic approach is decided upon, a team member is assigned to treat him, and another therapist commonly is made responsible for adjunctive service to his parents or family, though many clinics have the same professional person helping both.

Either *ad hoc,* on the initiative of the therapist(s) or routinely, after a fixed or prearranged interval, the team will reassess the situation and evaluate the extent to which progress has been made. It may then proceed to a closing of the case or a referral to some other source of what are believed to be necessary services which the clinic cannot provide. Cases usually are closed as "improved" or referred for further treatment elsewhere, follow-up is rare.

Although individual practitioners ordinarily have some measure of autonomy in the therapy process, diagnosis and terminal evaluation typically involve extended interdisciplinary discussion. Even in therapy, practitioners as a rule consult with one another regarding details of technique, intermediate goals, and the nuances of professional judgment. Not uncommonly, in working with a young child, it may be deemed therapeutically expedient to involve him simultaneously with both a male and a female therapist, though one may carry the principal responsibility. Although colleagues may cherish theoretic differences, "dynamic" approaches to personality are pretty much the rule, with psychoanalytic concepts, typically, the central point of departure. There is a single accrediting body; and it, together with a special interdisciplinary professional association, contributes a measure of ideological consensus.

A Court Mental Health Team

The mental team in a juvenile court typically includes workers from the same disciplines as those encountered in the child guidance clinic, though there may be somewhat fewer with interdisciplinary professional educational backgrounds. Judges, in particular, rarely have had any professional orientation in team practice or, for that matter, in any form of truly collaborative interdisciplinary relationship. Their very presence (not to mention their status) makes coordinating task performance, to say nothing of integrating it, quite a different challenge from that confronting a team in child guidance. Methods of practice, moreover, are noticeably different, and the atmosphere of any particular court in which a team practices may affect the work tempo of the team, intrateam harmony and the practitioners' ability to establish rapport with the children.

The team in child guidance usually addresses itself to the overall social adjustment of the child in treatment, even though a distinctive psychological problem occasions his appearance at the clinic. In theory, psychological operations under most children's court acts, many of them passed more than fifty years ago, reflect precisely this philosophy, too: the court's concern, by statutory mandate, is the child's life-style, and not the particular act which has resulted in his being caught "in the toils." In practice, however, particular judges may be especially fascinated by sex delinquency or by problem behavior in youngsters coming from marginal ethnic groups or disreputable families. As a result, the judge's demands for diagnostic workups may require the mental health workers to concentrate their energies upon a particular segment of the court's total caseload, not necessarily including those individuals whose behavior or situation they themselves might regard as most in need of explication.

Continuing contact with mental health clinicians may broaden a judge's knowledge and deepen his understanding of some of the aspects of disordered behavior. Such developments may occur, in particular, in settings where psychotherapeutically oriented colleagues make a vigorous effort to proselytize. Clinical personnel, in like manner, may acquire a measure of appreciation of law and legal process. Nonetheless, there has been considerable protest against judges who are adamant in their advocacy (and implementation) of scientifically untenable notions of psychodynamics. And there has also been some criticism of mental health workers who claim they are in a position to provide the indispensable foundation for judicial decision. Rarely are judges and mental health workers practicing collaboratively in the sense that all constitute a joint team.

Another peculiarity of work demands on a court mental health team is that the service process, initiated with diagnostic assessment, stops short at the point where the team puts a disposition recommendation in the hands of the judge. The team only rarely is given the opportunity to provide treatment it has recommended, even if the treatment should be within its own sphere of competence. Furthermore, the organization of the court frequently segregates the mental health team from the probation department, and it is by no means unusual for one social study to be written by a professionally educated social worker on the mental health team and another to be worked-up simultaneously and independently by a probation officer whose preparation for this work has been along quite different lines. Another anomaly of practice in this setting is that the court itself may assume responsibility for "supervising" children it determines to be neglected, delinquent or in need of care, if the judge in his "disposition" does not delegate the responsibility to a social agency or a correctional institution. But the "supervising" is usually assigned to the probation department, not to the mental health team which may have recommended supervision in the first place.

Perhaps the most distinctive aspect of team operations in the court setting is at the same time the one which is least constant: the part the judge plays on the team. In one court, the judge may have a mental health team articulated into the court's apparatus, but relate to it as though it were a separate department of the organization, connected to the bench but hardly intimately associated with it. In another court, the judge may participate informally in diagnostic conferences of the mental health team, contributing in debate to any disposition recommendation formally handed up to him; such a judge is also likely to be sufficiently acquainted with the special knowledge of mental health workers to address rather specific inquiries to them − in contrast to the judge who, as a matter of routine, merely "orders" a "psychiatric." A third court may have many judges, some of this latter type, others of the first type mentioned above. The mental health team serving this third court may find the court calendar arranged and rearranged in such a fashion that answers prepared for one judge's questions come into the hands of another judge who happens to be presiding the day a case recessed for further study finally comes up for disposition. This particular problem of interactions between the team and its milieu is discussed further in Chapter V; "The Team and the Complex Organization."

A Rehabilitation Team

The rehabilitation of the handicapped is a field in which teamwork practice has become increasingly common, especially since the end of the Second World War. A larger number of different disciplines is likely to be involved in this field than in any other where team operations prevail. In many settings, not a team but an entire staff may be the personnel unit, with the operation encompassing a plant of hospital size — the rehabilitation center. Since in this latter situation it would be a complex organization rather than an interdisciplinary team to which attention would be turned, we have limited ourselves to examining the case of the small interdisciplinary work group which does not itself incorporate workers performing custodial operations or those engaged in services to other workers rather than to clients. A rehabilitation service within a general hospital is such an interdisciplinary team; it may include professionals from more than a dozen fields.

In the hospital-based team, a physician typically is recognized as the team member invested with the highest authority; here, he may be an orthopaedist or a doctor who has been certificated as a physiatrist by the examining board for that new specialty. He may perform surgical procedures but commonly spends most of his work time examining physical disabilities which have impaired patients' ability to engage in normal activities, consulting with other doctors as well as colleagues in different disciplines and prescribing treatment to be provided by some. Inasmuch as rehabilitation quite commonly is a protracted process, he is frequently involved in long-range planning for referrals to extramural service programs. In some team meetings, personnel such as vocational rehabilitation counsellors not actually associated with the hospital may be involved on a regular schedule.

Hospital employees on the team include physiatric residents or other doctors, and nurses responsible for the care of in-patients. In addition there are physiotherapists skilled not only in massage and the supervision of exercises, but also in motivating patients themselves to carry on with the procedures deemed indispensable to an enhancement of their capacities. The typical team will also include a formally qualified occupational therapist, skilled in the selection of crafts or industrial-type projects specifically devised to increase neuromuscular capacities according to the patient's needs. A social worker, too, is a regular team member, responsible for rounding out diagnostic assessment with information from relatives and other outside sources, and for the various extramural contacts typically indicated as a course of treatment progresses. The social worker in a hospital setting commonly also bears the responsibility for the larger portion of personal counselling, discussing problems of the patient's social situation and post-discharge prospects.* A clinical psychologist may be a full-time team member, making formal contributions to diagnosis and planning and providing some psychotherapeutic services as well; and a psychiatrist may be available on a part-time basis, more commonly consulting with particular workers than with the team as a whole.

Rehabilitation's distinctive philosophy emphasizes the importance of coordinating assessment, treatment and evaluation along physical, psycho-social and vocational lines; at different stages, as a case develops, greater stress is laid upon one or another of these. Workers, to survive in this setting, must therefore be adaptable enough to accommodate to shifting work demands. Medical skills, for example, which may be most important at the outset, come to be essentially secondary at a point where vocational assessment, training and placement are the order of the day. In the hospital team, these last commonly are services to be arranged on a postdischarge basis, though they may be added to the patient's program while he is still an in-patient. In any event,

---

*We shall not detail at this point the ramifications of affiliation and responsibility common when a hospital social worker or occupational therapist is attached to a department composed of workers in his own discipline, over and above this attachment to the interdisciplinary team. This topic is discussed in Chapter V.

stress is laid upon reconciliation of a variety of perspectives, both in planning a coordinated battery of services in each case, and in helping the patient mobilize and sustain his inner resources over a protracted period — as rehabilitation proceeds from one intermediate goal to the next. Therapies are programmed to be concurrent or successive as the team may deem appropriate. A measure of out-patient follow-up may also be provided, but a hospital-based team is generally more apt to close cases on discharge, if necessary transferring them to other rehabilitation services in the community.

We have presented two sketches of teams described from an organizational perspective and three emphasizing substantive differences in work content. To conclude this chapter, we present a glimpse of the prospect confronting an interdisciplinary work group endeavoring to mobilize itself. The problem here lies in reconciling individual differences among the colleagues so that they contribute to the development of a novel enterprise instead of splitting it asunder. In the team described below, the variables of milieu, personal characteristics, group dynamics, technology and professionalism are interacting. To avoid confusing the reader, the team's articulation into a massive agency is not detailed here.

A Neighborhood Legal Advice Center

Mrs. Mary Brown, a thirty-two-year-old professionally educated social worker married to a lawyer, is the director of a new project to develop a store-front legal aid service in a ghetto neighborhood. A Negro herself, she is responsible for building staff that can provide a largely black constituency with a new and, she believes, much needed service. She and her colleagues will be helping disadvantaged people to achieve more satisfying relationships to the community as a whole. The focus of her staff's activity, she believes, should be upon problems with landlords, municipal civil servants, shopkeepers and installment purchase agents; Mrs. Brown and her clients live in a town where most of the people with whom clients come into conflict are white.

The new center's second, third and fourth staff members all join the staff the very same day; none therefore has seniority. Mrs.

White is another social worker, but a neighborhood resident, unlike Mrs. Brown who lives in a middle-class suburb. Mrs. White is forty-eight and has been a caseworker and a casework supervisor in public welfare for twenty-four years; she is active politically in the party dominating the municipal government. Dr. Green is a twenty-eight-year-old Afro-American psychiatrist who has just completed a residency in a mental hospital serving this neighborhood as well as others. He has agreed to work with the staff one day a week and is determined to provide services through his colleagues; acting as a consultant, he believes he can imbue the new program with the philosophy of community psychiatry, focussing upon anticipatory services rather than clinical treatment. Mr. Jackson, the third newcomer, is a fifty-eight-year-old white lawyer with twenty-five years' experience working with trade unions. He knows the neighborhood and has served for twenty years, first as a volunteer, then as a board member in the settlement house there.

From the outset, the team realizes it will have a big job deciding who will do what and exactly what the group as a whole is there for. It becomes apparent immediately that the two men conceive of the center as a community development project and believe the staff will bog down if it fails to reserve a sizeable proportion of its time for services addressed to the whole neighborhood rather than to particular people in trouble. The more experienced of the two social workers is determined to use the new project to help clients whom she identifies as "her" people, but one by one. The directing social worker is preoccupied with her administrative responsibilities; her concern is with building an agency to do a good work, but she has given little thought either to the details of division of labor or to the ideological crisis which impends.

A week after the hiring of the first three practitioners, Mrs. Brown employs Miss Gray, a twenty-four-year-old graduate of a predominantly Negro college, who has six months' experience as a public welfare caseworker. Two days later, Mr. Blue, a Negro neighborhood lawyer with a vestigial practice but well-known political ambitions, is hired; he tells Mrs. Brown he is fifty-five, but she suspects he is about ten years older. The same day she hires Mr. Johnson, a twenty-five-year-old Harvard Law School graduate who has just passed his bar exam, and Mrs. Wilson, who taught school in the neighborhood for ten years before passing her exams; both are white.

No sooner has the office opened than the staff discovers it has a backlog of disputes and litigation to cope with plus a major problem of orienting both its prospective clientele and the militant neighborhood woman the director employed as receptionist-secretary the very first day she herself was on the job. Who shall talk with people coming with problems and complaints? What position does the team take on "Black Power?" Shall the team meet weekly to discuss one another's problems or daily to discuss the work of the group? Should the center "reach out" to find people it can help, in addition to those asking for service; should it focus on criminal cases, on divorce and other family problems, or on work outside the courts entirely — dealing with the municipal housing authority and the county welfare department?

Since this is a sketch and not a case study, the team Mrs. Brown is trying to lead can be left at this point. This brief glimpse may suggest the diverse lines of inquiry to be pursued in developing an understanding of the situation and prospects of this project. Our own study of the variables characterizing interdisciplinary teams and interdisciplinary team practice now turns to the examination of the situation of the individual professional and problems of role definition.

Chapter III

HOW THE INDIVIDUAL WORKER
FINDS HIS PLACE

IT is possible to conceive of a team structurally as a constellation of positions, yet the team itself is not a concept but a group of persons. One of the constants inevitably encountered in an examination of any team in any setting is therefore that of "individual differences." Examining the scope of differential psychology is beyond the scope of this discussion, but any effort to describe characteristics of the collectivity must consider the impact upon the group of the distinctive characteristics of the individuals involved.

Problems centering about role definition are typical of interdisciplinary team practice. Traditional professional norms may more readily be accepted as role definitions where team practice has a long history. But in novel or changing settings, traditional role definitions are often incompatible with the recurrent demand that workers engage in certain activities which were once considered extraordinary.

More specifically, new work techniques may prove to depend upon the development of relationships not previously regarded as occupationally essential. Thus the nurse may be called upon to become adept at social psychology in order to cultivate the appropriate relations in "the therapeutic milieu" and the psychiatrist may have to learn how to work with a recreationist's distinctive "voluntaristic" conceptions of a patient's therapeutic involvement. "Head start" type preschool programs, to cite another example, may demand a new approach not only to parents but to the neighborhood; new types of positions are created and personnel from additional disciplines recruited. Insight into the bargaining processes in which roles are defined and redefined may be better achieved if particular interpersonal encounters are examined with reference to the specific performances each worker would like to demand of others.

As new practice goals are set, new teamwork patterns are evolved and new organizations are created to facilitate and coordinate practice. It does not take many decades before it becomes apparent that actions and ways of thinking once considered exceptional are becoming more usual, and tasks never performed by anyone just a few years ago must now be undertaken by or allocated to some particular person(s) as a routine part of a job.

It is small wonder, then, that roles (and the norms which support them) should be regarded as merely in the process of becoming defined. This clarifying of expectations is by no means a set condition that obtains in all instances; it is a process that potentially involves debate on role interrelations in each particular setting.

Despite ongoing role bargaining and a continuing process of role redefinition, the workaday atmosphere of a team comes to be pervaded by divergent notions about operations to be performed by the several members. Quite commonly there are about as many sets of expectations as there are members. Yet the practitioner who is uncertain about the "appropriate" way to behave, or who goes about his work in a way that varies from the expectations of others, may be criticized for impropriety. Some workers' implicit assumption that there is "one proper way" proves at odds with the realities of practice as commonly observed in interdisciplinary settings.

Some Individual Characteristics: Manifest and Latent

The starting point of any interdisciplinary practice team is always as association of persons. Individuals in configuration comprise the group, whether there is reciprocity of role expectations and role performances or not.

In order to understand the group's internal processes, and the way it practices are coordinated with those of other social units, some measure of understanding of characteristics of individual behavior peculiar to the group situation is indispensable. Each professional on each interdisciplinary team brings, along with his knowledge and skills, a personal history and an attitude toward his profession that is uniquely his own. He perceives the team's structure in a fashion dictated by his own insight and sensitivity; the team process impinges upon him only through his own definition of the situation.

Only those aspects of the self for which there is an organizational demand, however, can be occupationally relevant. The organization seeks the individual personally most likely to meet its needs as it defines them. The jobseeker enquires after positions whose demands he is happy to meet, positions presenting creative challenges in areas of work in which he wishes to engage, positions offering other incentives he finds rewarding. The compatability of team position and teamworker may be the outcome of a good deal of give and take, suiting the individual to the job and the job to the individual.

In practice, the position commonly is filled by an individual not regarded as optimally qualified, and the worker accepts a job only partly to his liking. Inducements of prestige, salary and security may prove as decisive as the opportunity provided a worker to employ the skills he prizes, or to enhance them. For some professionals, facilities, responsibilities and clientele characteristics are decisive; they are concerned with issues of task differentiation, work flow and the minutiae of interprofessional collaboration. For others, what is more important is the atmosphere of the work setting, the minutiae that make up relationships between personnel: the by-play at the coffee break may be scrutinized more intently than the contents of an organizational manual.

The extent to which individuals find organizational structures compatible with their own most cherished aspects of uniqueness clearly is related to a number of factors. Some prospective team members may be attracted by status differentials, which accord workers in certain occupations more latitude than those in others. Fluctuations in the labor market may impel organizations to "tool up" extraordinary practice conditions for particular individuals, inducements to select a particular position if many are available. Conversely, when workers rather than jobs are abundant, fewer inducements need to be offered by the organization and it is the jobseeker who is constrained to make himself appear especially desirable.

Personality traits and attitudes of a worker are presumed to be such as will reinforce his competence in the skills associated with his own discipline. Any questioning of the experience thus nominally accorded him may be taken by the worker as an occasion for offense. Professional associations can hardly be expected to refrain from endorsing work-relevant characteristics of their own members. This is the more true because admission to the association is dependent upon a more or less scrupulous certification procedure.

The occasions for personal insecurity under conditions of interdisciplinary practice nevertheless are manifold. There may be doubt as to whether or not one's colleagues share the same, or even quite compatible, professional values and aspirations. Likewise, there may be uncertainty as to the character of the work for which one may be held responsible and just who may be authorized to assign one various tasks. One may doubt whether or not his messages have been understood by a colleague or, conversely, whether he understands the colleague's message correctly. An individual may worry about the possibility of informal or formal evaluations of his performance by colleagues not competent in the same discipline. There may be concern about one's long-term career and the status among one's own professional peers. One may wonder if he will need to acquire new skills, including skills not commonly identified with one's own profession. Anticipation of demands for out-of-title task performance, or the assumption of responsibilities possibly not deemed professionally appropriate may also give rise to anxiety, to say nothing of feelings of insecurity.

Aspects of team structure and process in the practice situation may engender competitiveness or status striving in some practitioners. Worker dissatisfaction can impair the team's productive activity even where no overt conflict takes place; those who are disaffected may express repressed hostility in excessive passivity or flights of bureaucratic obsequiousness.

Of course, it can never be the "self" in all its complexity which is manifested in team practice situations. Social structure allows, or implicitly impedes, the development and expression of only some of each individual's unique characteristics, since only the "work-relevant" part of the whole person becomes engaged. The whole atmosphere of the work setting as well as the team's expectations — and those of its leader — all tend simultaneously to limit and to cultivate aspects of individual creativity.

An individual may serve on a team as an occupational therapist, for example, but he potentially offers the team, and its clients, far more than the essential range of skills which justify his professional identification. He may share with other therapists a capacity to offer either "industrial" or "arts-and-crafts" type projects, but actually be more skillful at one than the other. He may be basically qualified to contribute to joint assessment and planning, but his willingness to speak up in a group and his flair for articulating distinctive professional concerns are not identical with those of every other occupational therapist. He may have learned critical aspects of occupational presentation and demeanor, and he may have accepted in his professional indoctrination certain status differentials as virtually beyond question. Yet his response to leadership and to authority figures will also constitute a reflection of personality traits which long antedate his attainment of occupational skills.

This particular occupational therapist shares with others common professional qualifications including acceptance of human impairment and some minimal capacity to relate to the lopped, the disfigured, the infirm. But his personal warmth in cultivating rapport and his commitment to humane service will have roots in a life experience distinctly his own. The rapport and the commitment may be comparable to those of another occupational therapist or to characteristics of colleagues in other disciplines, but they will pervade his work in a unique way. His behavior will reflect an interplay of psychodynamics not precisely paralleled in any other man.

A last factor which we shall consider in our discussion is latent characteristics and attributes, since latent social roles, especially sex roles, affect the articulation of activities in multidisciplinary teams.

In one team, the social worker, for example, may be a woman, expected by her colleagues to be sympathetic, even motherly, in working with the individual toward whom professional activities are directed. She is expected to be willing and able to meet heavy demands; it happens that her idea of the job fits in with the notions of her colleagues. But not all social work positions are like that, nor would all social workers agree. In another team setting, the woman who is doing the social work job doesn't see it this way at all, yet her colleagues are agreed that she's making a great contribution; they're not looking for motherliness. On still another team, the social worker happens to be a man, sympathetic though definitely not motherly; his co-workers, as it happens, are often critical of what has been viewed as his overly sympathetic approach.

Another instance of occupationally relevant aspects of the female sex role is the affective component implicit in the therapeutically indicated activities of the nurse; if her approach to patients is womanly, her work may be better. Of course, there remains the question of the occupational situation of male nurses: it is at least debatable whether solicitude and tenderness are indisputably feminine qualities or whether the amount of expressive behavior expected of nurses is typically female. Much of the literature in psychiatry, psychological counselling and social work approaches these subjects without differentiating between the sexes.

Latent sex-role expectations, however, impede role performance in the case of mental hospital orderlies. "Manliness" in the orderly may suggest that obstreperous patients could be "manhandled," but this runs contrary to prevailing therapeutic ideologies. Consequently, manhandling becomes an occupationally illicit skill, although it may be esteemed in the orderly's peer culture and in the socioeconomic class from which most orderlies are recruited.

Socioeconomic background figures almost as importantly as sex among the latent social characteristics very commonly differentiating team members in a variety of occupations. In interdisciplinary discussions, the attitudes different professionals manifest and the underlying values rising to the surface may reflect variations in outlook between sons and daughters of clerks and small shopkeepers, on the one hand, and the children of corporate executives and wealthy doctors and lawyers, on the other. And those attitudes and values may prove at least as weighty as the more technical knowledge ostensibly apparent in discussing a problem involving workmen's compensation, say, or wife-beating.

Reference Group Behavior

Some insight into aspects of the personal background of practitioners may provide clues to the reference groups they adopt, the people to whose opinions they defer. Yet, of three counsellors who are Baptists, for example, the first may order his working life to values he ascribes to the Baptist community; the second, paradoxically, may concern himself not with Baptist norms but with what he believes Roman Catholics support and oppose; and the third may never refer to religious values or identifications at all in making decisions on the job.

In responding to demands his job makes upon him, each worker has in mind some constellation of task performance he believes his position properly encompasses. And he judges what is proper according to the beliefs and expectations he attributes to those with whom he associates himself socially. That is, he compares what may be asked of him at work with what he perceives to be acceptable to different kinds of groups with which he identifies; he appraises himself with reference to a variety of affiliations, many of them not of an organizational character. The outcome of such self-appraisal is really understood only if the nature of the comparison process itself is also appreciated. Because peer groups of professionals so commonly figure in discussions, it is well to recall that workers may also relate their actions to what they believe are the standards of nonprofessional (sex, age, ethnic or socioeconomic) groups, too.

Acculturation to the way of life of the interdisciplinary team may be accompanied by some attenuation of the individual worker's ties with distinctive professional organizations which served as primary occupational reference groups. As his ties to the group of original affiliation stretch thin, his occupational role may be perceived by his erstwhile associates as a repudiation, and a circular process of continuing dissociation and progressive alienation may ensue. The worker may thereupon develop a new professional self-image and turn toward different reference groups. Should there be no such groups, or should the possibility of affiliation prove negligible, the practitioner in a team setting may experience an identity crisis or suffer a period of social rootlessness occupationally.

Practitioners on teams not only compare their situation with that of colleagues in their profession in general, but refer specifically to those in team settings. Colleagues in other teams practicing as part of the staff of the same complex organization may constitute the reference group. Or colleagues in a higher status discipline may be the ones to whose values the practitioner orders his behavior; nurses and social workers, for instance, sometimes use physicians as a reference group.

Bureaucratic types may orient themselves to senior personnel of the complex organization in which their team practices, people who may in fact have a purely executive rather than a professional valuational system. Typically, a single social worker, psychiatrist, public health educator, and so on, becomes the exemplification of his discipline in the team at any given time; and even where two or as many as three workers "represent" the discipline, the probability of nonmodal types being encountered is by no means small. Reference groups seem to be brought into play more in transactions within interdisciplinary teams than in those activities which involve members with the outside personnel of the organization in which the team is situated. This may be related to the fact that interpersonal relations are more intense in small groups; another factor may be within the team. Interplay is more likely to generate crises of professional identity there. The kinds of transactions team members are likeliest to have with fellow employees outside their own work group are apt to be of a more routine character.

However, the extent to which various team members indulge a proclivity to compare their present work setting with others with which they are familiar — or in which they have personally been employed — is likely to influence both group solidarity and the status of particular individuals. Ideological reference groups may split a team right down the middle; half of the members of a juvenile court staff, for example, relating themselves to proponents of a philosophy of deterrence, while their colleagues espouse the values of those committed to rehabilitative approaches. And both factions may have ties with like-minded people working for the courts.

Moreover, as we noted above, each worker orients his planned activity not only to occupational-professional reference groups, but to imagined witnesses not concerned with the world of work in particular. Certain practitioners may order their ways to feminist values, for example, or to soul brothers in an ethnic group to which they wish to orient their own actions.

Each worker engaged in interdisciplinary team practice probably elaborates his own definition of his job and of the work situation in which he finds himself. That professional self-image may center about technical aspects or it may focus upon humane service concerns. It may derive from a variety of reference groups. Team unity is likely to be affected by the proportion of the staff dedicated to diverse systems of value; these systems, in turn, reflect the diversity of goals prized by reference groups to which the various team members relate. Teams bringing together one or another particular combination of workers may encounter ideological dissensions peculiar to their particular field of practice.

Values and Goals

The worker who is impatient with the narrowing bonds of his own profession's expertise can derive deep satisfaction from practice in an interdisciplinary team. He has at ready hand colleagues whose special skills pick up just where his own thin out. He can broaden his understanding of clinical problems through continuous employment of consultative resources which are a built-in part of the work situation, not something he must go to special pains to procure. He can be a party to ambitions and long-range service plans, and does not find it administratively necessary to close or drop a case merely because one phase of a treatment process has been culminated. And he has the continuing creative stimulation of inquiry and debate with equally committed people who approach the field with a focus perceptibly different from his own.

His work self, his skills and background, and his reference groups; all are vital to the part a worker plays in a team and the consequent effectiveness of the team's operation. Two more interrelated factors, equally vital, are values and goals.

Team interplay seems to sharpen the individual's propensities for self-criticism. So the worker who is oriented to both scientific and professional values may find himself scrutinizing possible contradictions between the two. Physicians, for example, must rethink the reconciliation of their commitment, on the one hand, to pushing back the boundaries of knowledge and, on the other, to the alleviation of successive instances of human suffering.

Those professional persons whose values and self-images are most deeply pervaded by the ideology of the scientist – clinical psychologists, for example – may at times find themselves in conflict with interdisciplinary team goals ascribing highest priority to clinical services. In the face of an administrative demand for speedy decision, they must riddle through for themselves how precise they will try to be when working on a case. In the crucible of clinical practice, ideals not only of thoroughness but detachment, too, may seem marginal.

The importance a worker attaches to professional autonomy will vary from person to person on a team, and probably also from profession to profession. Yet some workers may not be concerned about the matter at all. Though accorded greater latitude of judgment than nonprofessional workers, the professional, too, performs his tasks within a structure the society endorses. He is presumed to be endeavoring to achieve generally desirable goals through the employment of methods which are socially acceptable. His choices cannot be completely personal.

A worker may feel most strongly about what he believes is the uniqueness of his creative contribution to the common endeavor. Or he may derive simple satisfaction from being associated with a group that is helping people in need. Or his identification may be with the great institution in which his team practices, so that he sees himself as one of a brotherhood of healers even though his particular task is rolling bandages.

Values of professionalism sometimes find peculiar expression in the understanding of individual practitioners. Furthermore, the complex organizations in which teams practice not uncommonly have an ethic of their own, articulated or latent. In children's courts, for example, the unexceptionable practice of the confidentiality principle sometimes seems to rank highest, and occasionally individual professionals may bring the wheels of justice to a grinding halt because their segmental professional interpretation of the law's common mandate robs their own colleagues of crucial data. Nonetheless, the popular image in professional circles glorifies those who, like Judge Lindsey in the early days of the "social" courts, incurred fines or censure rather than disclose information shared with them as professional confidences. The "confidentiality" principle, nonetheless, though originally conceived as a guarantee of professional responsibility, can become a justification for reserving for personal use patient data potentially helpful to those colleagues perceived as competitors for social rewards. It may be converted from an instrumental value in the service process into a tool for status striving.

Ideology pervades team milieu, and observations about the prevailing ideology crop up in a variety of contexts. Task performance by the interdisciplinary team reflects the outlook and beliefs of individuals, but the team, in turn, influences individual values. Sometimes the professional goals of a worker come into conflict with the more limited objectives set by a team or its sponsoring agency. In a rehabilitation agency, for example, a problem arose because the social worker persisted in presenting to the team problems of clients who, though successful in the labor market, seemed to him "incompletely rehabilitated" because they restricted themselves to "sheltered" contacts in their social life; the agency's tradition focussed attention, on the other hand, on employability and job adjustment. A clergyman serving as a chaplain in a mental hospital had a similar problem, complaining that merely getting the patient back into the community ignored his deeper problems of cosmic relationship; the minister felt his colleagues should support his giving the patient a meaningful and purposeful life through the church community. In both instances the worker's values were not institutionally supported in the practice setting.

Just as a team may have a place for one member of a discipline and not another, its implicit rules may vitiate participation by individuals who persist in relating themselves to standards of particular disciplines.* There even are settings in which it is a condition of employment that workers abandon all traditional professional self-images and accommodate to the local legend that all therapuetic personnel constitute one single occupation.

The boundaries of permissible individuality in work style are often ambiguous, but there *are* boundaries, and team members whose creativity impels them to prodigies of innovation may confront virtual ostracism. In interdisciplinary team practice, as in any other social situation, different individuals behave toward it according to whatever may be their own particular perception of its nature. Any individual's attempt to translate his definition of his role into action may therefore precipitate a clash with one or another colleague in a team situation. And no amount of tenacity on the part of any one "performer" can really guarantee a colleague's treating him as he expects to be treated or accepting him professionally as precisely the person he perceives himself to be.

Frictions and disquietudes arising out of disparities among various team members' definitions of rights and obligations seem more the rule than the exception in interdisciplinary team practice. Reciprocity may be lacking in interdisciplinary relationships characterized by a persistence of marked status differentials. Even where the differential is small there may be some disparities resulting from differences in status, for all too often senior people have the "right" to expect performance of others without acknowledging any duty on their own part to reciprocate. Thus, a physiatrist in rehabilitation is commonly regarded as having the right to prescribe treatment to a physiotherapist; complementarily, it is the "duty" of the

---

*A worker's leaving may free the team of a burden, or deprive it of a seminal contribution. Turnover, furthermore, may simultaneously enhance solidarity and leave the more unified group substantially impoverished. When a substitute is hired, the organization is perforce involved in a "package deal;" it replaces a complete person with a different person. But the intention may be merely to provide a suitable performer in a more or less defined role in a bureaucratically conceived structure. In fact, the new worker may prove to be a very limited "substitute" for the one who has left.

physiotherapist to carry out the prescribed treatment. But there is a question as to whether the therapist may appropriately claim a "right" to seek the doctor's consultative advice as he works the case, and whether the physician may be regarded as bound by a reciprocal "duty" to respond. Where reciprocity is lacking or disproportionate, relationships are likely to produce tension, and a dynamic in the direction of change is produced within the team or within affected individuals. Sensitivity to status and salary disparities is a common problem among members of interdisciplinary teams. Workers on interdisciplinary teams are alert to what, in general, may be going on in a colleague's office. Remarks about differentials, e.g., in status, income or work loads, often reflect a pretty clear impression of the fellow worker's situation. Concern centers about what appear to be inequitous distinctions; those differentials which are in accord with commonly accepted stratification criteria may be regarded as just. However, by the end of the sixties questions were being raised even about such traditional "dividers" as the B.A. degree, in effect a racial screen.

The notable example refuting the classic approach to role definition is shown in the following discussion of collegial process at one "therapeutic community." Team processes in the 100-bed psychiatric Rehabilitation Unit of Belmont Hospital, as described by Jones (a physician), emphasized a playing-down of status differentials. Withal, it is clear that the operating philosophy was not simply the end product of a series of discussions and explorations on the part of a group which included two disablement resettlement officers, five occupational instructors, two psychiatric social workers and a psychologist, as well as the psychiatrists and twenty professional and nonprofessional nurses.

Final decisions on disposition were made by the doctor (and his patient); the doctor is referred to as being "in charge of the case." Describing changes in the activities and, consequently, in the status of the charge nurse, he observed that as a result "free direct communication between [the other nurses and the doctors] was encouraged." The doctor did not indicate who did the encouraging, but from the context it is clear that what is described is an implementing of the theory of the therapeutic community he, as leader, espoused.

Two of Jones' colleagues, however, pointed out that

> The way authority [in the unit] is exercised is highly variable. Senior staff members insist in some meetings that they have "only one voice in community affairs" or that "the group's decision is binding" and on the other occasions will discharge patients against group consensus . . . inaugurate or terminate group events and so on.

A study of doctor-nurse relationships in an American psychiatric team came up with similar conclusions. The physician-administrator claimed workers were equal in competence because they were equal "in humaneness;" but an assumption of unequal training simultaneously impelled him to doubt their real capacity to assume identical responsibilities.

Colleagues in other disciplines may take an interest in some skill characteristic of a particular profession; some may even have acquired it themselves. But in the last analysis, the very preservation of identity demands that the worker himself, or colleagues identified as belonging to his own occupational group, decide which techniques should be employed to meet any particular problem. In many situations, the very act of defining the problem involves skills which the worker may jealously reserve as his own to deploy as he judges best.*

In a discussion along similar lines, Neal Gross and his colleagues have spelled out the possible alternatives, as differences in expectations among incumbents of diverse positions become clarified in social process. Their rationale also explicates the seeming paradox of significantly different actions on the part of persons successively occupying identical positions:

> (1) An incumbent of a focal position may define what most of his rights and obligations are and an incumbent of a counter position may accept his definitions. (2) Incumbents of counter positions may

---

*Identification of the client and the objective of service may itself become a crisis in role definition for the worker. A social worker, for example, may find that his contacts are limited to "members of the family" of some particular individual identified by a colleague or colleagues as the focus of the team's work. If the social worker is theoretically oriented to serving the entire family as a single unit, he has some figure-and-ground rethinking ahead. Much the same may be the case with the psychologist who wants to offer group therapy in a team setting where there is an established policy, or an undefined tradition, of treating people on a one-by-one basis only.

define most expectations and an incumbent of the focal position may accept them. (3) An incumbent of the focal position may define his rights while incumbents of the counter position may define his obligations (or their own rights) and both may accept each others definitions of these role segments. (4) Neither the incumbent of the focal or of the counter-position may have well-defined expectations for each others behavior in their initial interaction and they may be eventually worked out through a trial and error process. (5) Some expectations may be learned prior to, and others during, position incumbency.

Organizational Socialization

The constellation of roles in any particular interdisciplinary team will be the resultant of an interplay of such factors as the clarity and forcefulness of role definition promulgated by a sponsoring complex organization; distinctive impacts of aspects of the previous professional careers and professional education of individual role incumbents; and the history of the team itself as an entity (turnover, for example, is an influence).

Employees seek to find a comfortable place within a system of work relationships. Finding one's place on the job often means developing loyalty to a subordinate unit (a particular team) rather than to the organization of which it is an organic part. Perhaps a parallel problem is the threat a variety of professional allegiances may hold for those (e.g., team administrators) preoccupied with cultivating solidarity within their team, whatever may eventuate elsewhere.

Repetition of expected behavior patterns is often regarded as providing an antidote to personal insecurity. But the extent to which one or another individual is distressed by unpredictability in his companions varies. People who survive the ordinary vicissitudes of intrafamilial competition may become quite disorganized in other circumstances where a partner's role definition and role performance are ambiguous and unpredictable. Participation in interdisciplinary team practice in an amorphous work situation may present precisely this kind of challenge to a worker whose rigid conception of individual integrity undergirds this whole sense of emotional stability.

The suitability of the individual to a role is more than a matter of capacity to meet job demands for specified occupational skills. Where fuzziness of role definition characterizes a setting, some workers can cope with their problems better than others. Moreover, a worker habituated (occupationally and characterologically) to complying with a decisive leader may be told clearly and truly that he is joining a team where interdisciplinary consultations are maximized but no group decisions are made until they can be by consensus. Although he understands the new role expectations well enough, he may find he simply cannot bring his special skill to bear on any but the most segmental problems, and that his productivity is shockingly low. A colleague, on the other hand, may be more readily socialized on this job because of his active desire to integrate his own approach to ongoing work with the plans of as many other team members as possible, as often as possible. Moreover, the colleague finds himself called upon to provide just the kind of help he likes to give. Yet the two workers may be equally proficient in the techniques of their calling, equally rich in experience, identically certified, equally well-educated.

Not all the skills actually employed by personnel in a given profession are given equal weight. Some are thought more important or distinctive (even unique); and particular positions may require performance capacities which are merely incidental in the work of the larger number of members of a profession in other settings. Thus, a judge in one "social" court may be in a position where clinicians' recommendations as to disposition of cases routinely impinge upon his decisions before he promulgates them, whereas his brethren on other benches are never formally obliged to accommodate their thinking to that of colleagues from other disciplines. Clearly, the definition of the judge's role and the characteristics differentiating the judge from persons in other occupations will depend upon the nature of the court in which he sits. His personal opinions about what a judge's role should be, to this extent, are constrained.

Among practitioners who have cultivated a strong sense of professional identity, a uniqueness as well as distinctiveness apparently is imputed to the vocation. Where role is "flexibly"

interpreted, and conditions of interdisciplinary team practice enlarge the areas of overlap to approach interchangeability, some workers therefore become anxious.

Charlotte Schwartz describes a not atypical difficulty when already-certificated workers were obliged to respond to a colleague from another discipline who was trying to cultivate a new philosophy of interdisciplinary practice. His advocacy of new work methods, new goals, new rewards, virtually a new role image, precipitated a crisis of morale:

> Nurses are trained to know what they are doing and why (or to believe that those giving orders know what they are doing) . . . The new role model underplayed intellectual knowledge and stressed emotional insight and "knowing your feelings" . . . In the old role, rewards stemmed mainly from approval by authority figures; in the new role, rewards were to stem from themselves, from their own feeling that they were helping patients. Thus, the new role was based on an assumption of a presumed self-sufficiency, a quality their past training had attempted to underplay if not to stifle.

Over and above his technical qualifications, however, the practitioner on an interdisciplinary team is commonly called upon to apply a sensitivity to the concerns of others, a degree of personal maturity in collegial relationships, an appreciation of the dynamics of group process — competence, in short, in interpersonal relations. One kind of fluency in interpersonal relationships that can contribute substantially to viable interdisciplinary teamwork is the ability to understand colleagues' educational-experiential background, their feelings and attitudes, and their conceptions of professional identity. By the same token, workers rigorously indoctrinated to value a particular system of interprofessional relationships may react with anxiety to practice situations where traditional role models are criticized and attempts are made to effect basic changes both in task performance and in professional self-image. When personality comes into conflict with established organization structure, it is not only personality that "gives." It is possible that the worker may simultaneously defend his own values and maintain a status within the organization while criticizing it; thus he contributes to organizational growth as well as to the maintenance of his own integrity.

Conclusion

This chapter has considered the interdisciplinary team as a work group made up of individual professionals. We have indicated first, some of the distinctive characteristics the worker as a person brings to the practice setting. Whether there are traits which might especially qualify a team member to assume the responsibilities of an expediter of group activity, for example, is one of the questions yet to be answered by empirical research; the literature to date either is vague about such matters or it presumes that occupational identity essentially establishes the potential of each of a group of colleagues. We have suggested the desirability of examining the relationship between labor market conditions and the kinds of compromises accepted by both professional people and those who engage them for interdisciplinary team positions; negotiations at hiring time might throw much light on hierarchies of value — what workers regarded as their strong and weak points, as well as the employee assets and handicaps emphasized by employers. Discussions of interdisciplinary team practice have noted that insecurity, even anxiety, is common among those staffing these work groups. Consideration of causation tends to contrapose intrapersonal and situational factors of both types. Conceivably, particular kinds of workers in specified occupations in one or another type of setting may be especially likely to experience more stress than they can sustain. Yet another variable in weighing individual differences when responding to the team situation is the character of the team, its structure and work style. This is a theme to which we shall return throughout.

The professional person serving on an interdisciplinary team, like workers in other settings, does not commonly have an opportunity to engage himself unreservedly in the productive enterprise to which he is committed. However, the fuzziness of role definition which characterizes practice of this type gives rise to a protracted negotiation process in which workers may enhance their status and achieve a more satisfactory reciprocity of duties and obligations. At least equally important, for these professional people, may be the achievement of some clarification of the contribution they will be permitted, or enabled, to make to humane service, and the range of creative activity the team will structure into their roles. Another aspect of the role negotiation phenomenon is the importance of the various reference groups with whom the worker identifies, and to whom he orients his on-the-job activity. Related to reference group analysis is the study of the impact of stereotyping upon expectations of workers' performance. Stereotypes may be most clearly a factor in the kinds of occupational role definitions initially presented to the worker, but latent roles (age, sex, etc.) also seem to figure importantly in the interdisciplinary team situation. This is another question requiring clarification, and, again, we suggest studies to determine whether team type or kind of setting are important as independent variables.

Yet another area of inquiry, in a sense paralleling reference group analysis, is research exploring interdisciplinary team members' resolution of conflicts of loyalty, assessing the overall "drawing power" not only of team leaders, but also of teams as groups. Such research, furthermore, could assess the influence of agencies with which teams are affiliated, and of the several professions. Related studies could pinpoint differences in the influence exerted by each, according to specific problem area, and possibly elucidate as well the particular type of worker* most likely to be subject to one or another influence in one or another area of activity.

It would appear that immensely frutiful inquiries may yet be made regarding the criteria to be employed in assembling any effective interdisciplinary team. We not only know of no studies on optimal size, but there have been no thoroughgoing comparative examinations of the impact of differences in sex or age balance, for example, to parallel similar studies in industrial settings. It is clear that in a number of fields where interdisciplinary teams are a common work unit, competing ideologies having cross-disciplinary appeal are prevalent; this suggests the desirability of examining differentials in the impact upon team effectiveness related to the ideological homogeneity or heterogeneity of the group. Such studies might also examine as a dependent variable the effect of an individual's subscribing to one or another ideology upon his status within the work group,

---

*We hypothesize that individual differences pertaining to other personal characteristics may be found to be independent variables as significant as professional identity itself.

identifying, in the process, such contingent variables as competition for leadership status and interprofessional frictions.

A strategic aspect of interprofessional conflict in teams seems to be the collision of workers whose role-model is oriented almost exclusively to professional values with colleagues notably more committed to the values of the scientist, or those of the bureaucrat. Processes whereby these three goal orientations are reconciled or contraposed, within persons and within the team, would seem to need further exploration. The value workers attach to professional autonomy and the nature of the latitude characteristically accorded staff in the exercise of professional judgment on the job are two more subjects deserving considerable elucidation. Values are also involved in the beliefs of individual workers concerning differentials in status within the group, not merely those related to professional identity but also any interpersonal disparities that may overshadow a "democracy of talents" on the job.

Attempts to clarify the distinction between instrumental and ultimate values of team members should eventuate in productive exploratory research. The same may be said of studies that might help identify indicators of team success, standards against which the colleagues presumably make their choice of the group pattern they deem pragmatically the most effective. It seems obvious that a hard way lies ahead of the worker who would set for the team, goals rather different, possibly more ambitious, than those to which his colleagues subscribe; yet the matter has scarcely been examined, despite its patent pertinence to the interest of scientists studying influence and compliance.

Processes of organizational socialization in the interdisciplinary team are of particular interest, since the team itself typically is as vigorously involved as the agency which may actually be the employer of interdisciplinary team members. The socialization of the worker, moreover, may be complicated by a conflict of loyalties to the team, the agency, or one or another profession, to say nothing of the distinctive allegiance owed the client. While there is considerable volume of general discussion of "interpersonal" and "group process" skills as desirable in interdisciplinary teamworkers, there still would appear to be a need for explicit empirical demonstration of the effect of such skills in expediting organizational socialization. Since the socialization of interdisciplinary teamworkers has been found to be a veritable struggle in a number of settings, attention might well turn to reciprocities in the socialization process, with appropriate scrutiny of social change in the institutions of the team and its complex organization host in the course of their efforts to clarify the division of labor with individuals.

And we might say that though any interdisciplinary team is in part a network of positions tied together by the devices for social control which ensure conformity to its normative system, it is just as essentially a social group with intrinsic psychological properties. Task performance in productive activities lies at the heart of the matter, but it is through the personal messages — implicit and explicit — exchanged among members, the expression of competitiveness, esteem, deference and so on, that team members carry on the interpersonal relationships implicity in the division of labor.

In the light of our understanding of the situation of individuals, the team's group approach to the organization of its productive processes is our next concern. We now examine the team as a work unit, its mode of operation and the systems for articulating individual task performance into the provision of group services.

Selected References

Brown, Esther Lucille: Improving staff motivation and competence in the general hospital. Newer Dimensions of Patient Care, Part 2. New York, Russell Sage, 1962.

Caudill, William: The Psychiatric Hospital as a Small Society. Cambridge, Harvard, 1958.

Frank, Lawrence K.: Interprofessional communication. Amer J Public Health, 51:1798, 1961.

Gouldner, Alvin W.: The norm of reciprocity. Amer Sociol Rev, 25, 1960.

Gross, Neal, et al.: Explorations in Role Analysis. New York, Wiley, 1958.

Horwitz, John J.: Dimensions of rehabilitation teamwork. Rehab Rec, 10:36, 1969.

Jones, Maxwell: The Therapeutic Community. New York, Basic Books, 1953.

Loeb, Martin B.: Role definition in the social world of a psychiatric hospital. In Greenblatt, M. (Ed.): The Patient and the Mental Hospital. New York, Macmillan, 1957.

56   *Team Practice and the Specialist*

Markey, Oscar B., and Langsam, Charles: What happens to psychiatric contributions in the juvenile court setting. Amer J Orthopsychiat, 27, 1957.

Rapoport, R.N., and Rapoport, R.S.: "Democratization" and authority in a therapeutic community. Behav Sci, 2, 1957.

Riessman, Catherine K.: Birth control, culture and the poor. Amer J Orthopsychiat, 38, 1968.

Schwartz, Charlotte Green: Problems for psychiatric nurses in playing a new role in a mental hospital ward. In Greenblatt, M.K. (Ed.): The Patient and the Mental Hospital. New York, Macmillan, 1957.

Smith, Harvey L.: Contingencies of professional differentiation. Amer J Sociol, 63, 1958.

Thorner, I.: Nursing — the functional significance of an institutional pattern. Amer Sociol Rev, 20, 1955.

Topf, Margaret, and Byers, Ruth G.: Role fusion on the community mental health multidisciplinary team. Nursing Research, 18, 1969.*

*Our own ideas reflect the contributions, published and unpublished, of several hundred scholars and workers in helping-healing vocations. Among these are several dozen who are listed above and following Chapters 4, 5 and 6 as authors of suggested supplementary readings.

Chapter IV

ORGANIZING THE WORK

ORGANIZING the work for which a team is responsible first and foremost means planning ways to provide professional services to clients. Human relations among colleagues may require special attention, but if the focus of concern is to be on the helped rather than the helpers, the essential questions have to do with task performances.

In situations where all the members of the team are substantially in agreement as to what the group hopes will be the outcome of its work, results are nonetheless dependent upon their capacity to devise some systematic approach to getting the job done. Effective procedures for checking both the quality and the quantity of "output" must be developed. It is not people's efforts and good intentions that determine team and individual success or failure; the ultimate test is whether things are actually going better for the person being helped.*

To ensure a satisfactory outcome, the work rhythms and work styles of various individuals must be brought into concordance and separate stages of parallel or successive processes have to fit into a grand design. The parts which make up the whole can, of course, simply fall into place by a happy accident. But more commonly, interdisciplinary teams (and the organizations to which they are responsible) plan work flow. Not infrequently, a work plan is set up for each case or job as a unique project, but more commonly there is a routinized procedure whereby various team members pick up the work at agreed-upon points along the line. Some teams, for example, map out a plan of operations for each case, *ad hoc,* at a formal conference before anyone provides the client any service at all on behalf of the team; all subsequent decisions in the

*In the case of patients on the downgrade, delinquents in process of reform, etc., "better" may mean "less bad."

course of task performance may be made by particular workers or by pairs of workers as treatment follows a routine course. But in other team settings, both work-flow and decision-making may be worked out in a very different fashion.

Personnel of different disciplines may be associated in work processes of an essentially "coordinated" character — successive or simultaneous operations which are independent though related. Or they may do the work by "integrated" processes in which activities of each interpenetrate those of all: conjoint operations are continual and there is frequent sharing or feedback of control data. In the mental health team, for example, diagnosis may be essentially additive, each specialist making a discrete, segmental contribution in a coordinated work process; or the resultant assessment may be synthetic, the outcome of a protracted discussion in which bits of data and partial insights are juxtaposed and integrated into one cohesive overview.

Where personnel of different disciplines contribute to a team diagnosis, it sometimes is possible to evolve a system of checks and balances. The team's standard operating procedure may be to encourage independent prediction of case outcome, and workers in various disciplines may present alternative plans for deploying the resources of the entire team. The practice situation lends itself to checking ultimate achievement against diverse anticipations that can be recorded during the assessment and planning phase. It appears, however, that teams are much more likely to put their heads together than (for example) to pit the psychiatrist's inferences from the evidence against those, say, of the psychologist. There has been little tendency to examine the influence of personnel of particular disciplines upon colleagues, much less to check differentials in prognostic skill.

Whether work is organized along coordinated or integrated lines, however, it is likely that the team will identify successive phases of their type of operation. Many teams also take steps to ensure some kind of formal or informal assessment of the relationship between outcomes and the work that has gone into achieving any particular result. The assessment of outcome may be a task undertaken by the team as a whole, by the chief (where there is one) or by the person carrying senior therapeutic responsibility for each particular case.

Assessment of the clinical situation at the time services are begun, or are first being considered, together with evaluations of case progress ad interim and at the time of discharge, represent just one type of task in which the team can coordinate contributions of its several professionals. There are several other aspects of the service process that present opportunities for combining skills, seriatim or simultaneously, or according to both designs.

But more than philosophical commitment is needed if tasks are to be laid out in such a manner that colleagues constitute a team operationally as well as administratively. The essential question is really neither one of attitude nor of relationship, though both are considerations; the ultimate determinant in judging whether work is teamwork must be how the job is accomplished.

There are a variety of technical advantages in turning over a job to a group of experts acting in association as a team. One of the most immediately obvious is the possibility of bringing a wide range of specialized skills and knowledges to bear upon the problems at hand. But of equal importance, perhaps, is the possibility of balancing man-hour resources at different levels of competence. It becomes possible to approximate a work situation where a maximum proportion of the time of each team member is devoted to tasks close to his highest level of skill. Concomitantly, his colleagues at their own highest level of skill shoulder responsibility for other tasks which it would be less economical for him to undertake. Interdisciplinary teams cannot be equated with work groups in general, since the establishment of an interdisciplinary team specifically implies that close and continuous collaboration of people with different skills and professional identification appear necessary.

In each successive phase of a service process undertaken by an interdisciplinary team, workers are not involved only with one another and the people they are helping. Their tasks also bring into the picture their several professional associations, plus the overall agency of which the team is a part and similar organizations throughout the community. In mental health settings, in rehabilitation of the handicapped and in the social courts, professionals recurrently find themselves comparing notes with colleagues engaged in similar work in other cities; and they find that in planning services they cannot be limited by the resources available within their own agency, since one or another kind of assistance that needs to be provided happens to be most available through some other organization. In concentrating upon the ways teams get their work done, it is therefore important to bear in mind that transactions with outside individuals and work groups may affect outcome materially.

It is important to remember that an interdisciplinary team may exist administratively as a unit on an organization chart without in fact ever really becoming an operational group. Individuals may be working away conscientiously, yet in the last analysis be working separately rather than together.

There are certain prerequisities to viable group interaction in a work context: people must be both willing and able to be team members. Team members must be willing to commit themselves; they must be really convinced that a pooling of efforts is worthwhile. Team members, furthermore, must be sufficiently commited to risk collegial criticism, a more or less continuous give-and-take dedicated to the improvement of what is perceived as a common enterprise. But participants who are willing must also be capable of participation. It might well be argued that when colleagues each contribute some bits of a mosaic they are not truly engaged in "discussion." A sharing of insights regarding the picture overall is an essential of true discussion; it is more than a simple additive process. Some measure of competence and knowledge, and an understanding that transcends the specialized expertness which may justify the individual's presence – all are indispensable if team people are to become truly "engaged" in the group's activities.

Yet each participant comes to the team with his own personal style in work, his own ways of thinking and talking, his own approach to the work situation and to people he meets on the job. Each profession contributes distinctive skills to the team's resources, but workers of different background may with the best will in the world have difficulty understanding one another well enough to put their heads together. Over the years, in each field traditions have defined typical ways of looking at problems, typical conceptions of what is important and what is incidental.

"Criteria of credibility" vary from one profession to the next; what one worker may accept as reasonably established fact may be dismissed by another as surmise. There are even consequential differences in practice stance, for one profession may substantially affirm a "care taker" responsibility while another has, historically, limited service to those actively seeking it.

It is desirable that the co-workers on an interdisciplinary team share a common goal (such as restoration of the physically handicapped to a fuller measure of social functioning); they may also subscribe to a common over-arching philosophy (such as the ideology of rehabilitation). But the tasks performed by workers in various disciplines are not simply variations on a single theme. The very reason for setting up an interdisciplinary team is that it brings together people whose distinctive skills differ. These differences constitute the essential rationale for the work group, even though there is commonly a measure of overlap of members' competences. Each colleague can couple a solid confidence in his own expertise with an equanimious acceptance of what he may personally regard as excursions on the part of co-workers. Such attitudes ensure that vital matters are unlikely to "fall between the stools" simply because people are fearful they will be accused of trespass.

Each piece of work performed by each team member may in some degree be facilitated or impeded by the activities of any of his colleagues. At any given moment in time, each worker's chance of doing his job as he sees it is affected by continuing development in the administration of the complex organization of which his team is a part. And as informal subgroups or cliques emerge, both within the team (if it is of any size) and within the larger organization, each individual worker's address to task performance may be affected.

Collaborative work by interdisciplinary team members is predicated upon some minimum consensus regarding the process whereby services are to be rendered. But before there can be agreement on process, team members must orient themselves to essentially similar, if not identical, clinical goals. Colleagues may, in fact, have no real interest in working together where there is radical divergence on objectives. Among colleagues jointly engaged in the rehabilitation of the disabled there may be debate concerning expectations that professionals should actually take responsibility for renewing the client's motivation if this wanes. In the "social" courts, workers may find themselves at odds in striking some balance between activities addressed to two different needs: those of the community and those of individuals before the bar of justice.

But confusions in the mental health and mental illness field are perhaps the most amply documented. A fundamental divergence of approach hinges on the selection of treatment or prevention as the prime concern. To this may be added debate about the contention that not individuals but social situations should be the subject matter of research and therapy.

Some measure of common understanding of division of labor is clearly desirable, but perhaps it is even more important to understand some of the implications of segmenting task responsibility. If those being served are the team's "cases" rather than the "cases" of one or another practitioner, protection against certain disasters can be "built in." The importance of such an understanding was dramatically exemplified in an incident at a community psychiatric clinic:

> A convalescent psychotic had been assigned a psychologist as primary therapist, but the relationship between the two never really took firm root. The patient complained to his social worker that the clinic was not responsive to his needs. In the absence of the psychologist, the social worker requested a psychiatrist to consider prescribing medication on the spot, because of the patient's erratic behavior. The psychiatrist responded that since he was not the primary therapist, it was not "his" case and would have to await some appropriate disposition the next day.

> That evening, the patient returned and broke furniture in the empty clinic offices. At a special staff meeting subsequently, the clinic director led a discussion on division of labor and the sharing of responsibility.

The Nature of the Collaborative Process:
Coordination vs Integration

It is our contention that a basic issue in understanding

interdisciplinary teams is the nature of the collaborative process. It is, of course, possible to approach this more or less philosophically in a discussion of values and ideals. Another, more psychological approach might focus upon the attitudes of workers, their conceptions of work, etc. But the heart of the matter appears to be the organization of the "productive" process — how, in fact, the work actually gets done. Our central concern, in short, is not with workers' aspirations, or even their ideas about what the job is or should be, but with the question of how people go about interrelated tasks in the process of helping clients.

No matter who may be participating in a work process, no matter what the setting, what the instrumentalities, no matter what the resultant service, the same basic questions always arise in studying the division of labor. Who decides what is to be done when? Who decided which worker will perform the task and what techniques to employ? Who helps whom to do what? Who decides whether a job is to be done at all, and how the work is to be divided up; and who decides whether a job has been completed satisfactorily?

We must differentiate the "interdisciplinary" team, in which each specialist has a solid general perspective and does his work as an integral part of the work of every other member, and the "multidisciplinary" team, characterized by independent services provided in what is basically a confederated milieu. Unfortunately, much more is really known today about workers' expectations and beliefs than about how teams get a job done.

Ways of working in some disciplines have historically impinged upon the content of task performance in others. Sophisticated observers have long been aware that experienced nurses, for example, subtly but nonetheless very materially influence the kind of care a doctor gives his patients and even his understanding of the nature of their complaints. However, in the case of certain other workers, the precise character of their technological engagement is defined a priori, e.g., the occupational therapist, whose very accreditation stipulates that both his own peers, and physicians, find him qualified to serve. Task performance in this occupation, furthermore, is expressly authorized by a physician's prescription only.

In the "historic" professions, a jealously guarded autonomy would appear to preclude any worker's undertaking to provide services in accord with a directive formulated by a worker in some other occupation. But the question can be raised in broader, more generic terms: how intimately is the work of interdisciplinary professionals affected by work performed by team colleagues? It appears that collaborative style is primarily a matter of the team's organizational approach to the work rather than the traditional stance of one or another profession.

The character of the collaborative process, we suggest, may be conceptualized as predominantly coordinate or predominantly integrative. In the former case, the autonomy of each worker within some defined practice area would be more jealously guarded, task performance by team members would in most cases be seriatim, or in parallel, and consultations would commonly be formally arranged − frequently, perhaps, to guarantee some concordance in essentially independent service processes. At the other end of this continuum, collaboration of the integrated type would be characterized by conjoint therapies and a principled endeavor to blur the borders of private preserves. Further characteristics of the integrated process would be collegial initiative in offering uninvited suggestions and comments to a worker; continual and informal consultation; a tendency to plan the service process as essentially a group undertaking from start to finish, with no problem area the exclusive concern of one member; and a general laissez-faire attitude toward the allocation of specific tasks to one rather than another discipline. In this type of collaborative process, the team's work might be regarded as organismic, different aspects being so intimately related to the whole as to be devoid of meaning if the integrating pattern were to abstracted. Conversely, collaboration of the coordinate type might be conceptualized as a structure in which each brick is an independent decision made by one of the associated, but primarily autonomous, professionals. Action taken by the team as a unit, therefore, might more likely be the outcome of a voting process in the coordinated work style, and of informally achieved consensus where the integrated pattern prevails.

The impact of these differences in outlook upon team work

processes is readily apparent. In coordinate practice "suggestions" may be welcome, but "criticism" is implicitly out of order. In integrated practice, the work schedule of all becomes the work schedule of each; without concordance of tempos, team process becomes an illusion. Some oscillation between the two work styles is conceivable. An integrated team, for example, may be able to survive certain substantial differences in work-style among members. A coordinated team may from day to day provide for very ample sharing of the work among like-minded, similarly involved colleagues — without compromising the autonomy of any. It is clear that types of interdisciplinary teamwork operations can be differentiated. They may be identified with reference to distinctive approaches to organizing the successive phases in providing professional services to persons, groups, organizations or communities. The question is not one of attitudes or relationships essentially; it has to do with technology.

A technological description of the processes involved in professional work might identify those individuals or social units to whose needs services are addressed as analogous to "materials processed."*

Process Analysis

In breaking down a service process analytically, it should be noted, steps can be conceptualized as entities, or they may be telescoped (two or more becoming one), or they may be subdivided — the subdivisions being regarded as entities themselves, in particular settings.† Furthermore, the definition of

---

*Passive human recipients of professional services may be regarded as analogous to materials subjected to productive manipulation in a process whose end product is goods or services; a body subjected to surgical manipulation may be regarded as essentially passive in this sense. The analogy, however, must be taken much less literally with reference to most of the professional processes we are discussing, inasmuch as the people involved are not only objects, but simultaneously subjects. While the client is a recipient, he is commonly in some wise also an active participant in the productive process. Despite such participation, however, he is not here regarded as a member of the team.

†The literature, particularly in the field of rehabilitation of the handicapped, features highly circumstantial and authoritatively couched lists of the steps in a service process. It should be noted, however, that the entire service in a particular setting may, by policy, center about a single step. This is the situation in a state public welfare programs with certain interdisciplinary teams whose entire job is assessment; mental health teams in social courts, likewise, are often limited to this single function.

process is itself a conceptualization: "beginning" and "end," for example, are clearly administratively identified in an organization setting. Furthermore, elements presented analytically as "successive" may in particular service situations be encountered "simultaneously."

Successive phases of a service process typical of interdisciplinary team practice are predicated upon a series of decisions. Some, for example, relate to the definition of goals or objectives, while others outline an overall plan for the deployment of professional resources. (The commitment of resources, in turn, is always predicated on a priorities policy, explicitly defined or implicit.)

The orderly sequence of operations is initiated in reception or intake activities. The team may itself decide exactly to which people, in exactly what situations and around exactly what problems it will provide services; or the decision may be made in the larger organization of which it is a part. Not uncommonly, policy which identifies categories, not cases, may be set by the larger agency or by the agency and the team jointly; but the clinical application of policy in the selection of particular cases may take place in the team. In any event, a case becomes a case in most interdisciplinary team practice situations only after two decisions have been made: first, a choice among possible intake policies and their adjunct procedures and, secondly, a determination that the clinical case falls within a class defined by policy as being appropriate.* In certain clinical settings, intake is a bipartite process: a nonprofessional worker checks eligibility in accord with criteria not requiring professional judgment, then refers a prescreened potential client to a professional worker. This may be an intake specialist who does no other work, or each member of the team in rotation, or a member of some designated subgroup of the team. In some settings, the whole interdisciplinary team acts as a joint intake panel. In other settings, a worker assesses the situation then makes a recommendation to the team, or to its captain, the decision not being made at the time of assessment. As noted above, intake policy may simply be that

---

*Strictly speaking, yet another decision precedes the decision regarding applicability of policy and the decision stipulating the policy be followed; a decision must first of all be made that a policy regarding intake is desirable.

clients of the agency are clients of the interdisciplinary team, or that clients screened and referred by the agency become clients of the interdisciplinary team.

After an interdisciplinary team has decided upon some sort of continuing involvement with a problematic clinical situation, a more or less formal study process of a diagnostic character is commonly embarked upon. A preexisting policy (the result of prior decisons) may govern the assignment of workers to undertake the indicated scrutiny of the problem, or a decision may be made *ad hoc.* Assessment not uncommonly is a multipartite process, workers of different disciplines developing and weighing appropriate evidence, each in a pertinent area of his designated specialty. A single person may be responsible for deciding upon a diagnosis* (and, implicitly, a prognosis). This may be either the leader or the clinical supervisor, if there is also a leader responsible only for administration. However, the decision in many settings is made by the whole team gathered in a clinical conference.

At the time a diagnosis is decided upon, the question of planning services likewise commonly is on the order of business. The team, or a designated executive, will commonly decide what indicated services can and will be provided, who will provide them and when. Sometimes a series of services is indicated; sometimes contingencies are anticipated and provision is made for reassessment of the situation after a designated period, or in the event of specified eventualities. In some teams, the plannning of services goes no further than the assignment of responsibility for clients to a particular worker, or subgroup of workers who provide on behalf of the team those services they decide are appropriate to the resolution of the identified problem.

All services provided after assessment and planning may be the responsibility of a single worker, or several may be involved, the process being divided into steps demanding skills ascribed to different workers. Consultations among the staff may be a routine aspects of the service process and such consultations may take the

---

*The medical term "diagnosis" is widely employed in the field; the outcome of the study process may alternatively be designated an "appraisal," "estimate" or "assessment."

form of formal staff or committee meetings, or informal, more or less impromptu discussions.

Progress on cases is reviewed at regular intervals in some settings, as specified stages of a service process in others; the review may be by the whole team or by a leader. After review, plans may be revised, and not uncommonly the initial diagnosis may be modified or changed, and sometimes cases are transferred from one worker to another as an outcome of reassessment.

Services may be terminated either because service goals have been achieved in relation to a situation, or because it appears no useful purpose would be served by carrying on.*

In addition to clinical evaluations on a case-by-case basis, assessment of the effectiveness of overall performance in serving a caseload usually is undertaken by teams on a periodic basis. In like manner, the performance of individual workers is usually evaluated at some point, though often it is a person in the team or in the complex organization who formally makes the critical judgments, and only rarely the team as a group.

Making Decisions and Judgments

Decisions may be made by individual workers, by the team or by the parent organization. Not uncommonly, determinations by different decision-makers conflict. But where clinically implicated decisions in interdisciplinary team practice are disputed, the distinctive characteristics of this particular system for getting work done quickly become apparent. Problems which everyone agrees are quite devoid of clinical implication turn out to be encountered only rarely. Conflict cannot usefully be resolved by resort to bureaucratic authority, though it seems this is often the first impulse of the uninitiated.

The crux of the matter is that the professional approach implies the exercise of a disciplined judgment. Decisions, in the

---

*Cases may also be closed because it is decided that better services can be provided elsewhere, because it is believed that the team's manpower can be more productively focussed upon some other problem, or because of policy or statutory mandates. Decisions to terminate a service relationship may also be occasioned by unanticipated staff or budget cuts; or the decision to break off may be the client's rather than the team's.

professional frame of reference, commonly follow as an assessment of evidence on which people of recognized and certified competence may validly disagree. And even the pragmatic test of a judgment's correctness is unacceptable, because professionalism implies that if the procedure employed is accepted as appropriate, or at least defensible, no colleague will be forward in making a judgment based solely on the outcome.

Decisions may resolve a problem on a specific occasion on its merits. Very frequently, however, decisions relate particular problems to already established policy; or they may be decisions to define a problem as one of a class and to formulate general policy for the class.*

Decision-making in different problem areas in different teams working as parts of different agencies, will be made within the confines of policies that vary considerably in rigor and comprehensiveness. Even where policy guidelines are available, decisions made within a bureaucratic frame of reference are likely to differ both in process and in result from those related to professional ways of thinking and acting. Colleagues of different professions go about making decisions in different ways; people who think so differently, though endeavoring to arrive at a consensual judgment, may be hard put to accommodate to one another's deliberative processes.

Where work is in some wise the joint undertaking of professionals from different disciplines, there may be vigorous efforts to develop a system to ensure a common basis for making judgments. But interdisciplinary discrepancies are almost a commonplace, for there may not even be agreement on "criteria of credibility" — that is, not only may the evaluation process and the criteria employed be essentially noncomparable, but colleagues on the same team may differ sharply as to the significance of "facts" which may be considered in decision-making.

Lastly, most professional people are accustomed to imputing an element of judgment to the decision-making process. They do not believe that facts speak for themselves. To professionals, assigning

---

*Or they may simply determine that a policy must be developed—such decisions clearly must precede both the other types.

a clinically unique case to a category — the cornerstone of policy application — is a fundamental exercise of that judgment in which their claim to expertness is embodied.

Task performance in helping-healing professions, as we have seen, commonly involves this element of judgment. Neither understanding of principles nor knowledge of specific techniques can be sufficient for any but occasional on-the-job problems. Indeed, it is his capacity to exercise an appropriately cultivated judgment that differentiates the professional worker from the technician. However, clinical insight depends not only upon characteristics of the worker himself, but also on the situation in which he practices. Specific institutional settings engender expectations that the course of action selected by the practitioners will be one of a specified range of alternatives; alternatives "out of limits" are unlikely to be recommended there.

To sum up, decisions must be made at each step of a service process. A team's work style — what it accomplishes and how it gets things done — will be very materially affected by the question of which organizational levels or echelons participate in the making of operational decisions. The atmosphere at work will be dependent in large degree upon the extent to which the team and its members actually determine events themselves. To the extent that crucial judgments seem to be made within policy guidelines imposed from without, morale may be affected. It also follows that if turns of policy vitally affecting the team are made by people at higher levels, operational decisiveness may be impaired. The extent of autonomy that must be regarded as indispensable has yet to be determined.

Team Size: Deployment of Manpower Resources

Certain group situations or events become possible only as the group reaches or exceeds a particular critical number. Conversely, there are occurrences which are impossible under certain numerical conditions. Frequent and extensive interdisciplinary discussions, for instance, are inhibited if too many disciplines are involved, even if each has but one representative.

Difference of opinion within a particular profession is less likely to come to the attention of a team if that profession is represented there by a single individual. Likewise, formal exploratory subgroup discussions, with presentation of reports to the team as a whole, are unlikely in a team of three. Or again, it may be easier to hold "a profession" responsible for a failure when one of its members, among several actually on the team, was the party involved. While his profession may be held responsible even in instances where it is represented on the team by but one person, this may be regarded as somewhat rare, since the full range of possible actions of "the profession" in that setting is necessarily limited to the actions of its "representative."

In small teams, the significance of numbers at once becomes apparent if the concept of supervision is examined. The composition of the group may demand a choice between only two alternatives: no supervisor, or supervision of one or more workers by a colleague from another discipline, a person most probably with limited capacity in the worker(s') area of greatest skill. In such situations, supervision is commonly administrative rather than technical; or it is presented in the guise of consultation — ostensibly without the authority of professional skills behind it. Nonetheless, occasions for formal evaluation of a worker's performance eventually arise, and an evaluation from another discipline must explain away the patently handicapping circumstance. Where a discipline is represented on the team by a senior practitioner and several others in inferior status the case is rather different. The difficulty then is likely to be encountered only when it comes time to evaluate the senior worker.

In interdisciplinary team practice, colleagues' divergent conceptions of the obligations of various roles become themselves the subject of debate. There is a difference, in short, between a professional person's being willing, for example, to waive the exercise of a commonly recognized prerogative and his willingness to stand back if the group denies his prerogative altogether. Thus, a psychiatrist may agree that colleagues of other disciplines take team patients in rotation, for psychotherapy, without formal referral from him. But the referral may be waived as a right of the psychiatrist which he consents to forego (and, therefore, by implication a right he may recover). Or it may be conceived as a work-flow procedure bypassed by the team, a formal detail not essentially tied into status differentials.

In order to enhance team flexibility in organizing the work, a specialist may consider developing certain of his own distinctive skills in collaborators of another discipline. Not uncommonly, however, he decides that in the last analysis they can only prove pale shadows of himself. This was the difficulty recently encountered in cultivating in public health nurses a distinctively social work approach to assessing situations; what happened was that the nurses tended to turn less attention to responsibilities in their own field which they alone were competent to assume.

It is often assumed that roles are unambiguous "givens," and that a "contribution" is made by each team member. However, the contribution each member is capable of making, or is enabled to make or will be permitted to make, is in fact quite commonly an outcome of debate and maneuver.

We have already discussed overlapping attitudes and procedures as problems in the process of role definition. At this juncture, however, we want to examine briefly its impact upon work processes. A basic problem in interdisciplinary practice arises out of the mputation of exclusive expertness in an area to one or another individual. While the rule is that it takes an expert to criticize an expert, the homely eventualities in day-to-day practice suggest that plenty of exceptions prove the rule.

Experts trained in one or another discipline are frequently very reluctant to abandon the prerogative of exclusive employment of their skills. Yet the possibility of reciprocity may encourage a worker in rehabilitation, for example, to relinquish certain activities to a colleague in another discipline, who may in some particular situation be in a position to do more for a handicapped person. Of course, this willingness to share is likely to depend upon workers' having an appreciation of one another's potential. In the mental hospital field, on the other hand, an understanding of psychodynamics and skill in interviewing techniques for purposes of psychotherapeutic intervention is today characteristically encountered in personnel of several different disciplines. An interdisciplinary team comprised, for instance, of psychiatrist, psychologist, social worker and nurse, therefore, certainly can no longer regard task allocation as a problem that will take care of itself.

Communication Networks

Team members may succeed in harmonizing their judgments around specific clinical problems, but what makes a "fact" a "fact" still will vary from one profession to another. This disparity of "criteria of credibility" can make for friction or, in any event, a measure of constraint; for example, in consultations between professionals who glory in their orientation to rigorous scientific values and belittle colleagues they believe are too easily impressed by isolated incidents. Another problem is exemplified in the work of one mental health team in a juvenile court. They recognized that the state reserved the right of decision to the judge but stressed the value of his becoming conversant with mental health approaches and views. No consideration was given to the possibility that mental health workers might profit from understanding something of law.

TABLE OF COMPLIMENTS

	That the Clinical Method is:	That the Statistical Method is:
Clinicians say:	dynamic, global, meaningful holistic, subtle, sympathetic, configural, patterned, organized, rich, deep, genuine, sensitive, real, sophisticated, living, concrete, natural, true-to-life, understanding.	mechanical, atomistic, additive, cut-and-dried, artificial, arbitrary, unreal, incomplete, dead, pedantic, fractionized, trivial, forced, static, superficial, rigid, sterile, academic, oversimplified, pseudoscientific, blind.
Statisticians say:	mystical, transcendant, metaphysical, supermundane, vague, hazy, subjective, unscientific, unreliable, crude, private, unverifiable qualitative, primitive, prescientific, sloppy, uncontrolled, careless, verbalistic, intuitive, muddleheaded.	operational, communicable, verifiable, public, objective, reliable, behavioral, testable, rigorous, scientific, precise, careful, trustworthy, experimental, quantitative, down-to-earth, empirical, hard-headed, mathematical, sound.

In *Psychology, the Science of Life* (Harper and Row, 1962), George Miller (following Paul E. Meehl), has laid out in a neat little table the conflicting images and self images of two approaches to the conceptualization of data acquisition.

What is known about interdisciplinary teamwork at this time suggests there may be no one best system for planning team service processes and carrying them through to consummation. The same may be said of communications networks: different patterns seem more suitable to different groups working under different conditions, and as its situation changes, an interdisciplinary team may be impelled to alter its system for obtaining, assessing and employing information.

The efficiency of a communications net will be affected by such factors as role expectations and the personality characteristics of workers sharing information. To these might be added professional attitudes toward the confidentiality of the service relationships, attitudes which may impel workers to limit the sharing of information. Furthermore, it seems likely that there is less communication in teams whose work process is essentially coordinated rather than integrated, just as information verification and correction (feedback) is more characteristic of communicative transactions in the integrated team.

Where the team's work proceeds according to an integrated rather than a coordinated scheme, one may hypothesize an emergence of increasingly pervasive patterns of synchronized interaction. As colleagues come more and more to share in one another's work, the most elliptical cues from one worker may suffice to elicit complementary task execution on the part of a colleague. Another aspect of interdependence is the "emergence" of products: several workers jointly providing another with partial and incomplete, but complementary, advice and information. The recipient in such a situation may be enabled to undertake some particular action himself, yet the outcome, strictly speaking, can best be understood as a team decision.

The effectiveness of intrateam communications clearly is dependent upon characteristics of senders, receivers, and of messages as well as of the situations in which people attempt to share facts, opinions and sentiments. Nuances of meaning carried by particular terms in the subculture of a particular profession may serve to transform the presumably common tongue into a foreign language for colleagues not specifically prepared for that subculture.

This "professionalism" which renders public language private may, of course, reflect some common school of thought to which practitioners from several different disciplines subscribe. Psychoanalytically oriented personnel, for example, can discourse freely about "repression" and "suppression" and with no give-or-take confusion, whether the communicators are psychiatrists, social workers or psychologists. But colleagues not conversant with the Freudian argot might regard these terms as synonymous, and receive certain communications only in seriously distorted form. The psychoanalytic ambience may not only engender private conversations in a private language, it may cultivate preoccupations with childhood-derived unconscious processes so pervasive that the ideas, aspirations and overt behaviors which comprise the "surface" of personality are neglected for examination of the depths. Practitioners with a different-world view will undoubtedly have trouble participating in a team dominated by this way of defining situations.

Explicit communications, written or oral, must of necessity affect the flow of work and the outcome of transactions among colleagues. Whatever the breadth of a worker's knowledge and experience, whatever his depth of penetration in "overlap" areas, the very identity of the other groups implies that there are mysteries to which he is not privy, techniques he cannot or has not mastered. Through communication, what was obscure can be made lucid. But team operations are also affected by interpersonal resonance and dissonance in conceptualization of, and technical attitude towards, day-to-day tasks. For example, a physician oriented to the patient as an essentially passive recipient of services may have difficulty attuning his thinking to that of a social worker whose professional rubric, "beginning where the patient is," bespeaks a rather different conception of the treatment process; similar conflicts may arise out of psychologists' criticism of "the medical model" in community service programs.

Messages: Form and Content

Within the team, unfettered communication may prevail and members may share interest in common problems, but there is no gainsaying the fact that it is ultimately not teammates but his own professional associations that attest to the competence of each professions "representative(s)" on the team. Persons not identified as members of his profession may join in his discussion of problems to which his discipline addresses itself, but they cannot, by definition, be fully competent to assess his judgment or proficiency. Identity is contingent upon there being a demonstrable knowledge base which the occupation claims as its own.

A psychologist, for example, may choose to acquaint his teammates with his reasons for employing a particular test as part of the battery he has selected to develop answers to a question put to him about a patient. But by definition he is the one most competent to decide which instrument is most suitable to the task in hand. Only another psychologist, presumably, should be capable of deciding whether, for example, a Rorschach, TAT or MMPI, is indicated — or all, or none. Whatever familiarity colleagues have with these instruments is, by definition, at lesser levels of competence. Their knowledge may conceivably be expected to be little more than would enable them to frame questions intelligently.

In the juvenile court setting, this very question may become a cause of contention. Mental health specialists, regardless of discipline, may question a judge's order for a diagnostic evaluation which gives no inkling of the questions which he hopes their report will answer. Judges, on the other hand, claim that contributions of reportedly competent clinicians are all too often materially irrelevant to the work carried on by the court.

Dispositions formally attributed to juvenile court judges may, in a sense, be looked upon as products of a team of mental health probation workers collaborating with the judge. Specialists have, upon occasion, effectively captured the authority formally vested in the one who depends upon them. Witness the mental health team described earlier in this chapter which implied that the adequacy of a judge's performance depended upon agreement with mental health specialists.

A pragmatic dilemma which occurs in court practice can well illustrate a problem encountered in a variety of settings. The sentence to be meted out to an offender may depend upon his judge's assessment of the likelihood of the offender's running beserk in the community at some time in the future. The judge may solicit a mental health team's prediction; his real concern is not with differential diagnosis ("paranoid or not"), and he is hardly interested in knowing which disciplines contribute to the assessment. His "disposition" is an administrative decision of an unequivocal character, and the "iffy" quality of a mental health team's prediction may be quite overshadowed by the kind of responsibility the judge is, by law, obliged to take. Withal, skill in formulating case-relevant questions addressed to his behavioral science consultants is itself a basic element of the judge's special skill.

Communications may reach the whole team or several individuals although formally addressed to only one practitioner. Messages coming to the team from without include (1) inquiries, reports, orders, etc., from the complex organization with which it is associated, (2) communications from other organizations in the larger society with which the team maintains relationships (e.g., associations embracing its field of practice, and service agencies working collaterally with individuals whom the team itself is serving), and (3) a variety of "inputs" from its own clients.

We shall touch upon the first two types of messages from without in succeeding chapters. We have no concern, here, with substantive aspects of the treatment relationship. Problems relating to the transmission of information to and from clients are therefore not discussed except as they figure in communications between or among team members themselves — which we examine below.

Communications among team colleagues include routine recurrent inquiries, requests and progress reports, formal channels through which the work of the team supposedly is expedited. These messages most readily come to the attention of any investigator, and perfecting their form is a continual concern of administrators and the conscientious practitioner. Interest has centered about expediting the transmitting (sharing) of information, and some attention has turned to the problem of formulating potentially productive intragroup inquiries and arranging priorities regarding response.

There seems to be a growing awareness, however, of the crucial importance of oral and subverbal messages. The inner life of a team is perceived more immediately around the water fountain or the coffee table, and in the fleeting byplay of informal corridor consultations.

The psychiatrist Jurgen Ruesch, in a sensitive and perceptive discussion, differentiated communications which are impersonal "station-to-station" calls (devoid of affect and usually circumscribed by occupational role), from "person-to-person" calls, in which the "role — the mask that somebody wears — is disregarded while emotional features become prominent". He remarks further that when "person-to-person" specialists have to deal with social institutions, large private organizations, or the law, communications may suffer disturbances. Bureaucratic organizations by their very nature are apt, in their communication practices, to do violence to the individual and "they [the specialists] tend to rebel or to withdraw from participation in organizations." It may be that Ruesch's personal values are illuminated by his additional observation that "the impersonal station-to-station call is used . . . on occasions when people wish to express their dislike for each other."

Bureaucratic temperaments may have a greater affinity for formal communications. At any rate, the bridling attitude of the professional toward bureaucratic work styles often finds reflection in the more "personalized" content associated with those oral messages for which no explicit plan is stipulated by the group. While oral communication is commonly more informal then written communication, a setting such as a scheduled conference predisposes participants to less spontaneous, more role-circumscribed communication. A yawn, a hard look, the muscular tension of one about to pounce — these subverbal messages, or message components, often provide the basic attitudinal note to which words add what might seem to be a more explicit communication but is actually an overtone.

Nonetheless, the subsystems and variant forms all are part of one web of communication: formal reports and control memoranda, to say nothing of pay checks; preplanned and *ad hoc* conferences and consultations; and the intimate byplay of role-peripheral contacts. Analytically, they may be examined in isolation. But against Ruesch's sharp contraposition of "person-to-person" and "station-to-station" calls, we would endorse the contention of Stanton and Schwartz that the two types of communication are complementary in effect. They say that the "formal and informal reports of the same incident may both be distorted," but that the distortions will usually be somewhat different; "distorted in . . . different ways for different purposes." And if a listener is receptive to both accounts, he may receive a more complete picture of the incident.

An especially fruitful examination of the part communications play in administrative process was presented in James Roney's case study of a county health department's twenty-man professional team. Identifying eight different types of communicative interactions as possibly characteristic of each pair of related workers, he found three notably different configuations: the "official" network; the network along which work orders actually travelled; and the complex of informal advisory connections. In the case of relationships where orders were ascribed to individuals by colleagues, the "ordering" individual disclaimed authority in 65 percent of the cases; and the same was true of 44 percent of the persons whom colleagues named as their "advisors." Likewise, leadership was denied by "the leader" twice and three times as frequently as it was acknowledged.

Performance Controls

The professional in private practice, while subject to certain constraints imposed by law and custom, may actually feel he is primarily responsible to the broad ethical framework of his discipline. He decides what kinds of cases interest him, how much time and effort it is appropriate to invest in a single problem, what kinds of records he finds most useful, and so on, subject primarily to the exigencies of the market place for humane services. Professionals employed by agencies in their own field (e.g., social workers) lead more regulated work lives, but the regulation is imposed by a more or less peer-dominated institution.

Professionals on interdisciplinary teams, however, may have to accommodate to work rules specifically designed to regulate essentially more complex service procedures. Controls must take more polyglot communications into account; and when compared with more homogeneously staffed programs, planning may be less likely to satisfy formal "reliability" criteria. The reason for this is that observations which conform to the procedural criteria of different professions are often inherently noncomparable, and in any event significantly different. Likewise, planning techniques that are acceptable in one profession may yield results essentially unlike those produced according to different techniques which another discipline has found more desirable.

The movement of problems (or clients) from one worker to another may require systematization. Serial processes in the office demand some sort of linear programming, and operations requiring the simultaneous presence of workers from several disciplines may require special planning. Case records may be kept by each worker; or there may be separate records supplemented by a common record, possibly in the form of summary notes. Workers may maintain their own liaison and job-expediting services, or there may be an expeditor-coordinator to keep the wheels turning. Ways of evaluating the outcome of individual and team efforts will probably be devised and they are likely to be formally complex, more so than procedures and forms that serve familiar purposes in single-discipline settings. Decisions will have to be made regarding the division of labor, the clarification of "facts" about cases, and so on; and some measure of common understanding of latitude in judgment accorded colleagues will be necessary.

Both sponsoring organizations and the lowest echelon work units establish controls of various sorts over levels of performance just as they endeavor to maintain quantitative output standards. But members of the several professions typically maintain quality norms which may be so inherently technical that it is difficult to explain them to nonmembers, even team colleagues of another discipline. Professionally distinctive record-keeping techniques, incidentally, may take on great symbolic significance for one or another occupational group; the voluminous narrative documenting social workers' clinical process is a case in point.

Where professional services are rendered by a group coordinating the contributions of workers from different disciplines, colleagues are in a position to afford one another, and the client, some protection of independent checks upon performance. However, a hazard is built into this advantage; while independent checks may reduce the likelihood of error and of performance becoming excessively routinized, there remains a possibility of the practitioner abandoning self-criticism and a rigorous professional dubiousness in the light of unreserved team endorsement of his judgments.

Error and failure must be regarded as normal eventualities in human affairs, so the capacity of an interdisciplinary team to carry on its work in the face of such contingencies may be one index of technological adequacy. The unsuccessful case and the catastrophe put the work group's evaluation and control procedures to the test. In addition, individual behavior in crises illuminates intrateam relationships, testing the viability of arrangements for the division of labor: crisis situations also evoke informal patterns of mutual support and provide opportunities to observe the team's willingness to encourage workers to run risks where these are professionally indicated.

The effectiveness of team operations might conceivably be objectively evaluated if it were possible to calculate the relationship of efforts expended to results achieved. Unfortunately, services provided by interdisciplinary teams are frequently addressed to problematic situations in which goals cannot easily be explicitly defined, and outcome seems to defy strictly objective assessment. Witness current debate with reference to pragmatic criteria for evaluating the effectiveness of juvenile court staff work. Recidivism rates are clearly too vulnerable to administrative manipulation. And the employment of formal indices of social adjustment precipitates a debate around the social values of ethnic minorities, which cannot be simplistically resolved in a society committed to democratic ideals.

In rehabilitation of the physically handicapped (to cite a different example), placement of the jobless in jobs is, as an index, susceptible to the same criticism that can be made of recidivism data in the delinquency field. Yet, to measure a rehabilitation process against the yardstick of "optimal physical, psychological, intellectual, vocational, emotional and social functioning," is to ask that the team achieve for the handicapped higher levels of adjustment than prevail among the populace as a whole!

Ideology

Whether a distinctive ideology is characteristic of each interdisciplinary team is hardly clear. It is, nonetheless, notable that teams in mental health, in the social courts and in rehabilitation typically claim partnership in the "movement"; in each field there has come to be a characteristic "philosophy," a set of values with which the team identifies or with which each team member is expected to identify. And one of the dynamics in the team's inner life may be debate reflecting crosscurrents within the field as a whole, crosscurrents of opinion not with reference to one or another discipline but to the processes and goals in which all are involved together.*

Yet the very gathering together of skills which helps the interprofessional team come closer to serving the whole man simultaneously tends to undermine the several members' individual grasp of the entirety of the service process. Systematic consultation and such formal enterprises as the multi-disciplinary diagnostic conference help bridge the gap. But the team system of work implies an articulation of disparate elements for the achievement of a previously defined goal: the service process is less readily grasped in its entirety. It may, of course, be argued that as a result of the "knowledge explosion" even the rarely gifted professional simply cannot bring to bear the range of insight,

---

*In rehabilitation of the handicapped, for example, it is an article of faith that the disabled client be seen as a "whole man:" he is not simply someone whose limited physical capacities place him at a disadvantage in the labor market—he is a father whose children want to look up to him, a citizen who wants to be consulted about community affairs, like anyone else.

understanding, knowledge and skill at the disposition of a merely competent team. Insofar as there are team consultations around planning and goal setting, as well as task performance itself, it may be that each colleague is ensured something of an overall view as well.

While team discussions may help workers to understand at the clinical level just what the small group is doing, the goals of the complex organization in which the team practices are set by nonclinical, or at any rate "less clinical" personnel. Furthermore, the goals such functionaries set for this larger system may stress servicing the needs of the organization as such, more than workers less preoccupied with purely administrative concerns would consider desirable.

Viewing the direction of development in still another way, personnel from different professions within an interdisciplinary team may entertain sharply divergent conceptions of the goals to which the group's efforts are addressed, and, consequently, the methods whereby the goals may be attained. This problem may be seen in a most remarkable form in the juvenile court. Few court workers today would endorse the colorful view of Judge Lindsey, who more than a generation ago found "society . . . a ravening wolf from which the weak must be protected [by the court's staff] and against whose attacks they must be made strong." Yet there are still those who see the court as a social service agency rather than one dealing with "equal justice under law." These people might decry the current tendency to limit the court to deciding questions of fact, with disposition and treatment responsibility in the hands of some other agency. While their rationale for the articulation of mental health services into the organization of the court was not quite in accord with what might be the consensus of expert opinion today, Lenroot and Lundberg, Lindsey's contemporaries, declared scientific study of the individual child to be indispensable, calling for a service that would "link together, check up and evaluate the results of the social investigation, physical education and psychological and psychiatric study." At the same time, Lou was calling not only for integrated multi-disciplinary assessment, but for full equality of probation and clinic personnel as well. What might not fit in so

easily with today's climate of opinion was his view that court
procedure might one day be entirely superseded by "medical
psychological, psychiatric and social technique." Yet Judge Polier,
just before World War II pointed out that:

> The substitution of clinics [manned by physicians, psychiatrists,
> educators and social workers] for the courts would not end the
> failure of local and state governments substantially to improve the
> conditions under which dependent children live. It would not assure
> either a more adequate probation personnel or a less niggardly
> support of preventive programs. (Polier, Justine Wise. Everyone's
> Children: Nobody's Child. New York, Scribners, 1941.

Much of the debate about teams' goals is related to substantive
issues, exemplified in our presentation by the "whole man" focus
in rehabilitation, and "justice versus social service" dilemma in the
juvenile court. The other frame of reference to which goals must
be related is the formal one: having set ultimate objectives, how
are proximate means to be assessed? In each interdisciplinary team
there will be some conception(s), explicitly stated or left implicit,
of the way(s) a team can increase the likelihood it will attain its
goals.

The very words employed by personnel from different
disciplines to identify the recipient of service are fraught with
emotional connotations, and distinctive professional ideologies are
implicit. The doctor's "patient," the social worker's "client," the
psychologist's "counselee," may be the same person, but in each
instance a particular word epitomizes a significantly different
conception of the helping relationship. In so far as the person
helped is perceived as being served by the team and not merely by
its several members, there is a need for agreement in this
connection.

Labor involves transformations in the material world which
produce goods or services needed by people. In the labor of
professional workers, the transformation commonly either is
"within" another human being or "in the social milieu" which
occasions need or distress in another person. As we remarked
above, it is immaterial to this study that workers in the helping
professions may be assisted, to a greater or lesser degree, in the
performance of their labors by people who are in fact the

recipients of service. What is germane, however, is that there are aspects of the worker's personal approach to his job which find such direct reflections in task performance that they must be taken into account as factors in the professional technology.

Conclusion

The overall perspective in this chapter has been upon task performance: distinctive problems in the deployment of professional manpower organized into interdisciplinary teams to provide one or another "helping or healing" service. We have focussed particular attention upon questions of getting work done. The distinction between collaborative work, coordinating essentially autonomous performances, and a collaborative style effectuated in a more integrated fashion is perhaps the key point in this chapter.

The most elemental questions regarding the technology of organization often remain unanswered in descriptions of interdisciplinary team practice. More must be learned about who decides who shall do what, when and how; and more must be learned about methods employed to assess the outcome of the group's efforts. Basic to an understanding of team technology, too, is a meticulous detailing of the successive steps or phases in the service process, with particular reference to the procedures employed in transferring a job from one worker to another. A careful observation of task performance and the analytic study of rationales of task articulation seems essential.

Decision-making and policy development are fundamental factors in the organization of interdisciplinary team operations, and ways in which the group goes about its work will be affected by the sponsoring agency's intercessions. The evaluation of performance, in particular, is a task in which the parent organization may be found influential. Employing productivity as a criterion, role conflicts can be examined with reference to the team's rather than the individual's interests. Productivity, likewise, is an indicator of value in yet-to-be-undertaken critical studies of optimal team size.

Studies of communications networks and the character of

information dispatched and retrieved in teamwork processes have already been undertaken, but much remains to be done. It appears desirable, in particular, that efforts be made to relate communication phenomena to differentials in team output. Information-sharing processes doubtless also affect life style and ways of work in these small groups.

The approach to the work, as well as the professional outlook of workers, individually and as a group, constitute a material factor in considering the problem of error and failure. This is an aspect of the work situation which at this time remains substantially unexplored. This question also bears upon the matter of team goals, and the impingement of broad ideological cnceptions upon the organization of productive processes.

Interdisciplinary teams, it is clear, are established because workers and agencies believe that collaborative practice promises more efficient service to clients; and, possibly, more effective, higher quality service as well. The way task performance on the job is actually planned, and the rationale of the division of labor are surely essential study topics. But surprisingly, these aspects of interdisciplinary team practice, so fraught with importance to clients and to society as a whole, have received probably the least attention in field research so far. What ways of working together promise an interdisciplinary team greatest effectiveness and which pattern is most promising under which circumstances? This is the basic question to which ongoing research may provide an answer.

Selected References

Argyris, Chris: Integrating the Individual and the Organization. New York, Wiley, 1964.

Bennett, Chester: Community Psychology. Brookline, U. Boston, 1966.

Cowin, Ruth et al.: Social work in a child health clinic. Amer J Public Health, 55 (6):821, 1965.

Geiser, Robert, and Rheingold, Paul: Psychology and the legal process. Amer Psychol, 19:831, 1964.

Horwitz, John: Education for Social Workers in the Education of the Handicapped. New York, Council on Social Work Education, 1959.

Lenroot, Katherine F., and Lundberg, Emma: Juvenile Courts at Work. U.S. Children's Bureau Publications, No. 141, Washington D.C., G.P.O., 1925.

Lindsey, Judge Ben B., and Evans, Wainwright: The Revolt of Modern Youth. New York, Boni & Liveright, 1925.

Lou, Herbert H.: Juvenile Courts in the United States. Chapel Hill, U. of N.C., 1927.

McCue, Cecelia: Team relationships in the rehabilitation process. Rehab Lit, 21 (3), 1960.

Modlin, Herbert, and Faris, Mildred: Group adaptation and integration in psychiatric team practice. Psychiatry, 19, 1956.

Roney, James: A case study of administrative structure in a health department. Human Organization. 24 (4):346, 1965.

Ruesch, Jurgen: Disturbed Communications. New York, Norton, 1957.

Rushing, William: The Psychiatric Professions. Chapel Hill, U. of N.C., 1964.

Stanton, A.H., and Schwartz, M.S.: The Mental Hospital. New York, Basic Books, 1954.

Stuecks, Alice: Working together collaboratively with other professions. Community Mental Health Journal, 1:316, 1965.

Wiener, Daniel and Raths, Otto: Contributions of the mental hygiene clinic team to clinic decisions. Amer J Orthopsychiat, 29, 1959.

Chapter V

THE TEAM AND
THE COMPLEX ORGANIZATION

THIS chapter is devoted to a brief elucidation of various aspects of the connections between teams and the larger administrative units within which they operate. While many elements of these relationships are familiar to students of administrative science, we suggest that both the "line" work groups and the practitioners typically involved present distinctive, if not unique problems in organizational development. Both the team and the agency are likely to be confronted by a number of operating problems inherent in this particular structural linkage but rarely, perhaps, encountered by one or the other save in this context.

We shall endeavor to identify in the following pages a number of questions concerning the formal character of a team's ties to its host agency. The two collectivities are potentially incongruent in some respects. Conceptions of the work itself and of its goals are frequently debated; they are the next matters considered here. We proceed to a somewhat more detailed treatment of the dimensions of interaction between a work team and the bureaucratic apparatus characteristic of a complex organization. Following the delineation of bureaucratic relationships, attention is turned to some characteristic ways in which the work life of the individual team practitioner may be affected by the larger setting – and the ways in which the individual worker, in turn, may make his mark on the organization as a whole. The chapter concludes with a discussion of evaluation/control procedures, and an inquiry into the reciprocal influence of team and complex organization upon one another's policy-making processes.

Articulating Subunit and Unit

Interdisciplinary teams are most commonly encountered in

large service agencies or institutions, i.e., in organizations whose staffs are not made up entirely of professional workers practicing in small work-groups. While the larger unit's reasons for existing may be substantially the same as the team's, this is not always the case. A fair proportion of the complex organization's total staff and budget are allocated to various "maintenance" functions, e.g., plant, personnel, audit and control, records, rather than to the helping-healing processes with which the team is most likely to be concerned.

Bureaucratic administrative procedures in the organization of which it is a part will necessarily be reflected in the team's own operating methods, since the systems for authorizing activities and reviewing their outcome must both mesh in with the way such matters are dealt with at higher levels. The mechanisms of sanction and of social audit, as well as other policy-serving regulations of the complex organization, find reflection in work rhythms, even in practice style at the clinical level. Work schedules, reports and statistics, even such basic questions as defining the beginning point of a continuing service process — all involve transactions between the team and the institution under whose auspices it operates. Yet some of the concerns of complex organization administration: effectiveness, turnover, morale itself, find reflection in team process and not only as effects; team activity may generate reaction and change at higher echelons.

Since the larger organization is a significant part of the social ambience in which the team functions, the capacity of officials at the top to project institutional commitments relevant to the professional values of rank-and-file practitioners may have material impact upon the team. The destiny of the overall organization is, in the last analysis, dependent not merely on day-to-day policy-serving decisions, but on the broad social ends to which the enterprise must periodically be reoriented. This process, whereby the larger entity conserves its distinctive character and cultivates institutional integrity, affects the opportunities of subunits, teams and workers to achieve their own goals.

To understand the ways in which its parent organization affects the life of the team, something more than a study of the larger setup's structure is indicated. The organizational setting within which the team practices contributes an atmosphere which is itself a reflection of the community and the surrounding culture. The spirit that prevails in any particular team's parent agency is also a function of the large agency's goals and technology. Organizations have their own "life styles;" operations at the team level are affected by more than purely structural considerations.*

A variety of indicators may be employed when studying the character of a team's connections with its host agency. Among these we might mention an examination of the volume and the character of communications between the two; the extent of which work input and output of the team passes through the complex organization, as well; and the absorption of team people (especially "captains") into the overall hierarchy of the complex organization. Where parallel units within the same agency can be compared, differentials, in turnover for example, may suggest noteworthy and essential differences between teams ostensibly engaged in the same kind of work. Similarly, changes in the overall organization may find reflection in fluctuating indices of the situation in different teams.

While various studies give some glimpses of teams' internal procedures for input-output control and the evaluation of the productivity of the group, one might well imagine from much of the published material that sponsoring agencies simply provide office space and foot the bill without making any significant inquiries regarding the work for which the group is individually and collectively responsible. The administrative dimension has not been concealed, it simply is tangential to the concerns of most investigators who have interested themselves in interdisciplinary teams. Investigations of information-sharing and feedback processes following messages back and forth between an interdisciplinary team and other component parts of a complex organization, don't compare with the amply documented studies of such phenomena within the team itself.

Teamwork processes and inner dynamics clearly are affected by

---

*Issues of considerable moment may center about such questions as the color of a worker's smock, In many hospitals, status differentials among staff are symbolized by distinctive uniforms; one can even distinguish a convalescing patient from visiting friends and relatives by the fact that he alone wears bed clothes.

the volume of reports and other control devices employed within a complex organization to maintain surveillance over input-output relationships. The effect, however, may be diluted in organizations characterized by poor internal communications nets. Where information moves slowly, or messages commonly are misunderstood, control processes are affected. Good communications make central control easier, and facilitate the team's reporting what it desires to and is able to report. Impaired communications, however, by no means guarantee impaired control and therefore greater team autonomy. The result, on the contrary, may be more capricious and arbitrary exercise of whatever powers are reserved to the larger organization. A case in point is the nature of the linkage between time controls over worker absence and tardiness on the one hand, and the paymaster's office on the other.

A wide variety of transactions involve continual, more or less expeditious crossing of the boundaries between the interdisciplinary team and the rest of the complex organization in which it is ensconced. Both the hiring and firing of personnel are usually processed through the larger agency. Salary levels must be set there, and some delineation of policies affecting vacations, office space and equipment, travel for professional conferences and the like must emanate from the same quarter. Yet even the more extended field studies are surprisingly silent on administrative aspects of the relationship between professionals in interdisciplinary teams and the agency which in the last analysis so materially affects their day-to-day work lives.

The sponsoring organization affords the team an endorsement more comprehensive than any mere certifying body could provide. It is, or is supposed to be, in the business of regulating, systematizing and expediting. In many instances, the larger administrative unit also is a more explicitly defined system than the team, and constitutes a source of stability in the latter, especially in situations where role definition is still an urgent and continuing task within the team.

The complex organization may present the team with explicit job descriptions. But contributions to role negotiation also take more subtle forms. As already noted in our discussion of roles, the complex organization may feed reports, work assignments, paychecks, supplies, etc., into the team through a designated leader. Where the leader's status and authority are in question, it may be the complex organization that confirms the legitimacy of his power. Furthermore, it may help him by making the connections between the team and other parts of the organization easier to see. The leader's activity as liaison between the team and the complex organization thus may ensure his status among his colleagues.

Where interdisciplinary teams with one member indisputably occupying the most superior status are articulated into the structure of a large complex organization, problems of "latent interest" may arise. The top person on the team may be preoccupied with professional concerns and may see his own interests as essentially similar to those of his colleagues. But if the complex organization demands he be an administrator, his position may in fact demand that he defend team staff cuts should overall organization chiefs decide they seem necessary or desirable in some larger frame of reference. Or his status may give rise to a latent interest in discriminatory allocation of travel funds: for example, budgeting that reflects invidious prestige differentials rather than any operational needs either of the work group or the organization itself.

There has been little exploration of the possible impact upon the larger unit of an already existing work crew transferring in as new employees. While personnel are more commonly recruited individually and as relative strangers to one another, the pattern of a "package deal," by now not unfamiliar in research programs, is not completely unknown at the clinical service level either. A related, and probably more prevalent, practice is the understanding that the employment of a senior clinician implies his right either to hire colleagues ("assistants") of his own choosing, or perhaps to nominate them, with the understanding that the hiring will be consummated unless the personnel department of the larger organization turns up some very substantial objection.

Money matters, too, rarely figure in discussions on interdisciplinary practice. But, contrary to classic definitions of conditions prevailing in bureaucracies, it does appear that some agencies have negotiated a flat budget for the interdisciplinary team when hiring a leader or captain, the understanding being that he might exercise a measure of discretion in setting salary levels for different positions. And there have been situations in which a prospective team captain made his acceptance of an employment invitation contingent upon stipulated persons being hired at set salaries to work along with him. One may imagine such incidents to some degree affecting the internal balance within a much larger work force.

In any particular setting, the type of leader who will prove most useful to a team in expediting the achievement of its objectives may vary according to the measure of autonomy retained by the group in the conduct of its affairs. The scope and intensity of interrelations with the bureaucratic apparatus of a complex organization likewise affect team performance; and much depends on the stage of development of both team and sponsoring agency. In some situations, dynamic, aggressive team chiefs may be welcomed by administrators of the larger unit; in others more passive, stay-at-home types may be sought. The very survival of a team may depend upon the congruence of its leading personalities with those encountered at higher organizational levels.

Ends and Means

Goals and values of administrative personnel may contrast sharply with those of workers in the helping professions serving on teams in the same organization. Scientific expertness applied to work content may come into conflict with organizational expertness focussed upon essentially administrative rather than operational concerns. There is a very real difference in perspective between workers whose central concern is output of services and those preoccupied with procedures, the way things get done.

The larger unit frequently has different goals from those of a team. For one thing, it may embrace teams of different types; purely clinical teams, those combining services with research and those pursuing research interests only. Or the complex organization may be designed to achieve certain of its objectives through other processes carried out by employees organized into basic units of a more homogeneous type. And, overriding all, there is the "system" goal: the overall unit's pursuit of activities designed to perpetuate its own existence. The system goal of course may elicit more energy input at the top than down at the team level, but a team altogether uninterested in the larger organization's concerns is living on borrowed time.

Evolving conceptions of the mission of the host organization, what has been referred to as "commitment" can become the focus of sharp ideological debate within interdisciplinary teams. And both productivity and morale may be affected by developments within the larger entity, which tend either to subvert the team's homogeneity or to disrupt the coherence of outlook in these work groups which are actually engaged in the provision of services. The larger agency may be disinclined to support certain kinds of practice innovations which teams may deem necessary or desirable; small work groups may be willing to take responsibility for risks which a massive establishment deems a threat to its "image."

Whether a community mental health center, for example, should concern itself with treating mental illness or preventing it is a philosophical ideological issue; but it is encountered in interdisciplinary teams as determining which on-the-job activities shall consume what proportion of interdisciplinary time.* Similarly, in a rehabilitation center the ideological issue may be whether the handicapped are to be served until they have achieved unimpaired social functioning in all areas or merely with reference to employability. In a children's court, to cite yet another field of practice, debate may center about defining the enabling legislation's intent: justice or social service.

Sterotyped allusions to the pervasive problem of the professional within a bureaucracy commonly focus upon struggles for autonomous exercise of judgment regardless of inflexible routines. Such formulations can hardly be criticized as incongruent with the realities of contemporary practice in

---

*It may also become a determinant of the composition of the interdisciplinary team itself.

large-scale organizations employing interdisciplinary teams. But the implied conflict cannot be regarded as an administrative inevitability. A newer theory of bureaucracy propounds a system institutionalizing the exercise of judgment, rather than the classic doctrine of consistency in application of specific rules. It is recognized that in many jobs efficiency depends on review and continual revision of operating methods. Executives can help the organization achieve its objectives more effectively if they concern themselves with results rather than with enforcing compliance with traditional technique and procedure. And such leadership evokes group creativeness, ingenuity within the work team. The challenge to administrators at the policy level then becomes one of achieving organization goals, transforming projected needs into a dilemma which lower echelon executives are induced to resolve by innovations at the operations level.

Certain policies, both formal and administrative, are likely to be set at the overall organizational level, and only their instrumentation is left to the team. As noted previously, teams may be directly involved in decision-making through some sort of representative procedure, or may be free (even encouraged) to make recommendations. The question of which policies are to be formulated at team level and which elsewhere is itself a policy problem not infrequently the subject of heated dispute.

Thus, if the team is obligated to raise some proportion of its budget, both the decision that the team be a source of funds and the decision as to the proportion of funds to be provided by the team itself become possible occasions for policy conflict. The likeliest team source of funds being client fees, an additional occasion for policy debate arises: who sets the fee schedule and how are critical decisions to be made? It is likely to become apparent that fee scaling (and possibly fee determination) are most expediently a central-office function. The team, however, may be questioned about the proportion of "charity" patients accepted at intake, if it makes its own intake decisions.

An essentially similar debate around policy and its implementation may arise if a team seeks additional personnel, and the parent organization (perhaps for the first time) questions productivity. Or a team may become involved in grand debates looking toward a definition, or a redefinition, of the goal(s) of the larger organization in which they practice. We have already cited some of the opinions expressed in discussions of the mental hospital as a "therapeutic community."

Similar conflicts come into focus in considering the part different staff members should play in a children's court. The contention about the appropriate location of mental health clinical services is by no means unrelated to differences of opinion regarding the court's nature. It has been called "an institute of family relations with the force of law behind it." But an increasingly prevalent view stresses the court's concern with fact-finding and the administration of justice; counselling and social services are regarded as questionable in a court of law. Administratively, the question becomes one of the qualifications to be expected of court personnel, and the point at which the expertise of ancillary personnel should most properly be introduced. Not uncommonly, teams in children's courts are articulated with the rest of the organization at the judge's office, either bypassing the probation department or maintaining only tenuous and *pro forma* relations with it. Less than a decade ago the overwhelming majority of probation officers had no specialized training. The mental health professionals, therefore, had an apparently objective rationale for their superior status.

Bureaucratic Structure and Procedure

While complex organizations in some ways resemble other collectivities, in theory at least they typically are characterized by highly formal interpersonal relationships and a notable explicitness and specificity in schedule and routines. The activities of individuals are consequently more strictly ordered, and written rules define permissible and expected behavior quite explicitly. To administrators believing in such relatively closely hedged bureaucracies, processes of role bargaining, which as we have noted seem characteristic of the inner life of interdisciplinary teams, may seem anomalous and disorderly. Senior administrators may be nonplussed to learn that day-to-day task performance in an interdisciplinary team is not quite in conformity with what they might have supposed were job descriptions of its personnel.

In actual fact, however, as we have noted, modern organizations no longer are set up as classic bureaucracies (if classic bureaucracies in fact ever did exist). Despite efforts to centralize top decision-making, administrators at intermediate levels increasingly are authorized to exercise authority at their own discretion. Furthermore, a measure of autonomy and latitude in the employment of individual judgment is a jealously guarded prerogative of professionals; even in bureaucratic settings their independence dies hard. In the case of interdisciplinary teams, payroll titles and salary status may be quite unequivocally stipulated, and a table of organization may even show which position incumbent has authority over which. But relationships actually prevailing within a team may reflect great role ambiguity, making the official organization chart a mere figment of some senior bureaucrat's imagination.

It seems rare, however, for administrators on the outside to feel impelled to bring the division of labor within a team into conformity with some sort of theoretical blueprint applicable to the organization as a whole. Hospital executives, for example, have deliberately endeavored to experiment with a number of teams organized formally along divergent lines. On the other hand, there have been agencies whose directors have come to the support of traditionally oriented interdisciplinary team captains beset by innovators determined to redefine authoritatively sanctioned roles.

There seems good reason to doubt whether the classic picture of a rational, efficient bureaucracy characterized by division of labor according to specialized competences, systematic rules and impersonal hierarchical authority is the best model for understanding certain great public service enterprises whose staffs are dominated by personnel from the historic professions. Where scientific and professional knowledge undergirds the authority of high status functionaries, the power of persons in senior positions is limited by something more than the legal or quasi-legal authority with which the bureaucrats are invested. In practice, decisions commonly are made not merely according to rule, but in the light of best professional judgment. Thus, in a hospital, subordinates are not only permitted to contradict superiors; but in the case of physicians in charge of a case, they are under professional mandate to exercise their own best judgment even where this involves rejection of the counsel of an expert.

For the practitioners comprising an interdisciplinary team, instances of difference of opinion on professional grounds may arise not only within the group but between the group and senior administrators in the complex organization of which the team is a part. In such situations, shared professional identity often helps team leaders in the complex organization to come to terms with one another.

Conflicts arise out of discrepancies between professional and bureaucratic evaluative procedure; the two approaches to control are essentially incompatible. But the interpolation of the interdisciplinary team as a type of work unit within a complex bureaucratic organization may tend to make the professional's work situation less anomalous. Much remains to be learned about the ways in which the team accounts to the host organization, but it does appear clear that the salient controls over practitioners are for the most part exercised by the team. Where a leader exercises such authority, it is couched largely in the language of responsibilities not to the complex organization but to the interdisciplinary team and its clients.*

A common problem of administrative design arises, however, where workers are simultaneously members of an interdisciplinary team and of the staff of a functional department in a complex organization. For example, a social worker who is one of the staff of a mental hospital ward being run as a therapeutic community is also a part of the staff of the social service department of the entire hospital. It may well be that above all, such workers should be responsible to the team's leader and to their interdisciplinary team colleagues, with no dual allegiance to any executive or administrator elsewhere in the larger organization. A senior person and department colleagues in his own profession may nonetheless enhance the contribution a team member can make to

---

*The recipients of service, of course, may be perceived as clients of the worker, the team or the agency; this varies from setting to setting. "Vested interest" in the client itself becomes a determinant of structure and process within the team, and impinges upon the content of the team's relationships with the larger organization.

interdisciplinary team operations at his own work place. Where departmental allegiances do not undercut team ensembles, intraprofessional consultations provide an invaluable amplification of the team's own resources; but if the team is the primary instrumentality of service, the validity of departmental structures must be measured by the yardstick of usefulness to the team. If one particular profession is, or has been, dominant in a setting, workers in other professions may feel a need for one or another departmental organization, and a "chief" in their own disciplines as a protective power center and a focus of distinctive professional identity.* Traditional bureaucratic charting may set up an hierarchical structure regulating a large treatment organization. Yet behind this "ghost," the real "skeleton" is articulated in such a way as to leave each of a multiplicity of interdisciplinary teams the highest degree of autonomy. Perhaps it would be most correct to recognize the prevalence of two kinds of internal process: one (backed by strict hierarchy and more rigorous control of individual's performance), operating a range of "supporting" services such as personnel, accounting, perhaps even clerical and records; the other (more like a confederation of interdisciplinary teams with a superstructure as much consultative as in command), dedicated to the substantive organization of services to clients. Operational processes arising out of the confederative structural pattern permit the several teams a wide latitude, and control over individuals is delegated to the lowest echelon almost without reserve.

Where an attempt is made to introduce innovations such as interdisciplinary team practice into organizations already characterized by rigidity, traditionalism and a high level of authoritarian or bureaucratic structures, difficulties are encountered. The new work style was resisted in a number of well-established mental hospitals, for example, but found easier acceptance in clinic programs where it could develop as the larger organization itself evolved.

*Blum and Downing (1964) have presented a report tracing the history of three interdisciplinary teams created in a county health department on the initiative of its director. Two teams were developed by extracting staff from already operating departments; torn by workers' old allegiances, these were beset by turnover, complaints and work delays. But the going was smooth for the team representing a new project, unburdened by the competition of tradition-rich parallel units.

The dynamic situation of an interdisciplinary team within a larger organization may reflect the extent to which this particular structural form prevails throughout the agency. Child guidance clinics, for example, are organized around the activities of one or more interdisciplinary teams, but a court may carry a team as only a small part of its total staff and budget. Understanding of team work methods and accommodation to team requests for one or another exceptional administrative practice may be related to the size and influence of the team operation in the overall situation.

The Individual Employee

Persons cherishing images of themselves as classically "free" professionals may approach interdisciplinary team practice as antiorganization men. The lawyer is accustomed to working out his own schedule in planning time he'll put in on a case; the doctor may find it odd that his best opinion is pooled with that of specialists who aren't physicians at all, so that the team can develop a common approach to his patient's problem. The most elemental details in typical complex organization work routines — the time clock, the clerical pool, the form to be filled out in multiplicate — all may provide occasions for symbolic protests reaffirming the integrity of the individual. On the other hand, there are specific work procedures which take on institutional meaning for members of a profession; to tinker with these invites a collapse of any solidarity prevailing at the operations level.

The public health educator routinely considers a variety of media as he plans communications with a population at risk, and a team directive to employ TV, say, to the exclusion of word-of-mouth contacts might be viewed as an intrusion upon his area of expertise. By the same token, a clinical psychologist knows which instrumentalities he deems most appropriate in assessing the ramifications of a behavioral problem brought to his attention; he knows how to structure a testing situation, and how much of a battery he wants to employ — any structuring of the work which constrains his exercise of best judgment in these areas is likely to be experienced as an on-the-job stress.

Contacts between interdisciplinary teamworkers and other

employees in a complex organization involve relationships of two kinds. Problems arising in direct connection with services the interdisciplinary team is set up to provide may occasion consultative contacts with nonteam employees in the same disciplines. And the need for technical support outside the compass of clinical helping and healing may lead to relationships with workers serving in "staff" capacities in offices serving the complex organization itself. If the interdisciplinary team itself has a captain, administrator or staff services specialist, such contacts may be funneled through that one individual. The individual who emerges, or is designated as a leader by the parent organization, will have his own distinctive problems of relationship there.

Interdisciplinary teamworkers, perhaps those with administrative responsibilities in particular, may come into principled conflict with the organization of which the team is a part. In debate around questions both of goals and of structure, they may ultimately contribute to changes not only in the content of their own jobs but in related offices on various echelons throughout the organization.

In the process of establishing a new agency where much of the work will be of an interdisciplinary character, the reference groups with which senior personnel identify help set the tone. As teams are activated, line staffing patterns and interprofessional status differentials are more or less clear reflections of the relationships that obtain among the men at the top.

Since the larger organizations which most commonly figure as sponsors of interdisciplinary teams tend to be agencies broadly dedicated to values characteristic of the professions, leaders and officials up to the very highest levels frequently are professional people. As the overall unit relates to the universities which educate its future staff and the professional associations to which its present staff belong, it may therefore be represented by persons who share both background and values in a sort of interlocking directorate. The professional identity of top echelon administrators may be blurred, but it is frequently hardly questionable.

In the case of teams whose host organization is dominated by a particular discipline, it is also important to recognize that the work of the entire group and the performance of each specialist's every task will be in an atmosphere pervaded by the subculture of one profession. To staff who are themselves of that occupation, the norms of the setting may be accepted as "natural," being familiar. To others, the prevailing expectations, values and traditions, will be more or less alien; they are confronted with an acculturation problem. A psychologist in a court clinic is likely to have much to learn about the powers of judges and the impact of an authoritarian work setting upon his own approaches to people identified as "offenders." By the same token, a social worker practicing in a school or hospital setting has to approach family contacts in the way the host institution has made customary.

The professional's services must not only meet the standards set by his colleagues, but also satisfy the continuing pressure of the demands of laymen. The physician in his private office can anticipate patients raising questions he as a doctor may not be able to answer: e.g., the range of community resources to which a mentally retarded adult may be referred. Patients will also call upon him for medical economics counsel at the very limits of his range of expertise. Practice under organization auspices commonly affords a built-in buffer against such pressures from clientele — in particular, economic stresses to which a market economy gives a measure of free play.

Assessing Efficiency

On a day-to-day basis, workers may largely engage in activities as though they were responsible only to themselves or to colleagues in parallel status. Interactions on the job may involve little by way of impersonal bureaucratic relationships. Nonetheless, formal restraints are present, and, though held in reserve, they tend to influence informal behavior. A professional person in a team setting is likely, if unsatisfactory, to run up against sanctions imposed by the organization or its representative on his team; while those responsible for the overall operation may bring outside consultants down to the team level upon occasion, problems with individual practitioners are unlikely to want handling by professional bodies or other extramural resources.

Individual workers' standards of professional integrity and ethical commitment to clientele may nonetheless collide with tempo and productivity demands of the team or of the complex organization in which it practices. Colleagues in any profession pledged to clinically individuated services might feel called upon to manifest a concern with the personal uniqueness of each client and a commitment to move at the pace that client sets, regardless of progress norms set by others. But many social workers, for example, would be loath to affirm a preeminent commitment to the individual client if this were interpreted as placing his health and welfare above the welfare of the community. In team practice settings, such dilemmas are by no means inconceivable.

In the preceding chapter, we indicated some of the problems encountered when professional workers undertake to assess the acceptability of a mixed group's output, to say nothing of the difficulty implicit in determining the adequacy of each individual worker's contribution. Confusion may be worse confounded when evaluation is in the hands of "outsiders." In the sponsoring agency, an effective bureaucracy may have a variety of devices for assessing the relationship between the input (dollars and manhours) and the output of services to which the agency is dedicated. These control procedures may or may not be appropriate to an interdisciplinary team's activities, and there is a possibility of friction on this account. As is the case with so many kinds of conflict, the outcome of disagreement may be a mutual clarification and the development of more appropriate criteria of efficiency, as well as more suitable rating procedures. Such conflict may, however, eventuate in a schism, either between the team and the larger organization or within the team itself.

Policy Development and Staff Services

The team's conduct of its service operation, as well as the manner in which it conducts its internal affairs may fall within the scope of overall policies of the complex organization. When a novel problem suggests the formulation of a new policy for the guidance of the group or individual team members, the complex organization may even be found to have a policy stipulating the steps to be taken in determining whether a new policy must be formulated, a new procedure devised.

The team's life within the organization will therefore be subject to a measure of regulation: first by the policies prevailing within the larger unit; second by rules or executive judgments determining which policies are applicable to the team, and in what degree; third by the extent of participation in administration and policy determination accorded the team (e.g., through representation on higher echelon policy and control committees).

The complex organization, rather than the team, makes both the final decisions regarding information policy and the determination of what media will be employed to bring the availability of team services to the attention of possible clients in the community. Concerns of team members or of the group with reference to overall characteristics of clientele, or reaching a new constituency, therefore commonly filter through a complex organization procedural screen.

The precise mode of operation of the complex organization as a buffer between team and community remains virtually unexplored. Certain tasks, for example, are performed by receptionists, or for that matter, by the security staff; very different ones by the board of directors. Discussions of interdisciplinary team practice have centered about problems of clinical policy and operations. But concretely these unfold almost without exception under the aegis of a philanthropic or governmental agency. The question of who has a "right" to be served by a team, for example, may be answered one way in a context of administration and organization finance, and in a possibly different way if the context is one of professional ethics.

"Routine" administrative actions, "trivial" revisions of procedure in a complex organization may have great impact upon the inner life of an interdisciplinary team. Each administrative decision, each action, is in effect a message; and the communication may carry an "informal" freight in addition to its manifest content. Dynamically, communications depend in large measure on the relationships among the people involved. A worker, for example, who believes that those in his profession are accorded little deference by the organization, may become quite upset by a reassignment from a twelve o'clock to a one o'clock lunch hour. The message, as he receives it, has little to do with lunch; he feels he is being prevented from associating with "the powers that be."

Clinical personnel preoccupied with services to confused, unhappy, suffering people are notoriously impatient with many tasks popularly associated with the concept of "the organization man." Job descriptions, annual reports, requisitioning for office space, budget presentations, equipment maintenance and fiscal controls are matters beyond the ken of many professionals and certainly beyond the interests of most. As individuals become acquainted with the bureaucratic "ins" and "outs," however, a sense of team unity may overshadow their marginal allegiance to the larger ensemble.

Nonetheless, salary continuity must ultimately undergird any continuity of team services under most operating conditions prevailing today. And in mass society, attention to "housekeeping" detail is a price of survival, whether "big brother" is a philanthropic foundation, a community chest or a governmental agency. Even a team engaged in private group practice must provide for some manhours (their own or a guest expert's) addressed to keeping the structure in order.

Preoccupation with stability, "order" and integrative structural forms can so freeze the inner life of an organization that creativity and innovative interpersonal relationships are discouraged. In many complex organizations, therefore, self-protection suggests that although the very broadest definitions of policy may be made at the suprateam level, freedom of judgment in specific applications be left to the team, or its leader. This may include, for example, the practical rights of decision — sometimes called "recommendation" — in the hiring and promotion of professional staff. Transfers, as between teams, and discharges, however, may be out of the team's hands. Furthermore, it is not uncommon for senior clinical personnel representing teams to take some hand in certain administrative affairs of the complex organization, and, with the passing of time to become more and more concerned with administration and less and less with the clinical problem in detail.

Just as complex organizations vary in the extent of autonomy permitted their interdisciplinary teams, they differ also in the activity areas they reserve completely; areas considered inappropriate to operations at the team level and those in which stipulated activities are proscribed. Fiscal controls over and above the petty-cash level, for example, are commonly reserved as a central office function; interorganizational relationships, e.g., community agency contacts directly by teams, on the other hand, may be permitted, subject to policy directives passed along from the top.

One of the central administrative functions the complex organization may provide the team is a continuing public relations program and appropriate measures both for publicizing the team's work and protecting some measure of privacy. The central office also commonly takes an interest in the professional good name of the team and its individual members; the agency has a stake, willy-nilly, in the reputation of its employees.

The host agency is vulnerable in some degree to criticism or attack in dispute related to questionable professional judgment on the part of team practitioners, to say nothing of outright malfeasance, not, after all, an unthinkable contingency. Insofar as the employees involved are members of professional associations, the larger organization in which the team serves may find a stout ally both in defending itself and in disciplining a culpable employee. Of course, the "ally" may play a very different role in the event of a member professional who complains of being abused by senior officials.

For most interdisciplinary teams, the structure and procedural patterns of the sponsoring agency are simply "givens." But developments in an organization may be generated out of the interplay of a number of change-patterns superimposed one upon the other. One possibility well worth exploring is that the structural procedural innovations an interdisciplinary team may be impelled to make (or to importune the sponsoring organization to promulgate) may interact with the prevailing order of things in the larger enterprise in such a fashion that the interdisciplinary team in effect changes the host agency. By the same token, any basic reorientation or change in organizational priorities at the top is reflected in policy review and alterations in overall developmental patterns which may, in turn, affect the life and work of interdisciplinary teams.

Conclusion

All in all, the complex organization may be said to provide the main ambience of the team's work life. The team's immediate concerns are the output of services to the particular clients it contacts and the processes whereby it transacts its professional business. But as we have suggested above, a multiplicity of particulars must be agreed upon before broad structural principles can be defined.

Communications between the interdisciplinary team and higher echelons of the agency in which it functions may not flow smoothly in precisely the same kinds of channels provided elsewhere in the organization for other linkages between line and staff; furthermore, a distinctive feedback system may be indicated for the team as a special kind of unit. The whole question of transaction across the boundary between team and complex organization has been left virtually unexplored, and substantially the same may be said for the distinctive aspects of the team leader's relationships with nonteam workers elsewhere in the organization. Much remains to be learned about the impact of the larger body's budgeting process, and it is possible that new perspectives in administrative theory may be opened as we learn more about the absorption of new personnel who join a large staff as a work group having a prehistory of its own.

It would appear that the goals of agencies, even those "wholly" devoted to professional services, are upon occasion probably at variance with those of interdisciplinary teams within them. Yet the host organization has for the most part been described as a "gray eminence," its purposes and distinctive problems obscure, a sort of featureless platform in which the team does its work.

We would lay particular emphasis upon the desirability of ascertaining in some little detail the ways in which bureaucratic authority may impinge upon professional judgment, and what eventuates when the two collide. A literature around this question is already extant, but it is in the context of essentially personal conflicts; the apparatus, and the team as a factor is rarely implicated. We have touched upon the problems involved in conflicting expectations of team members on the part of colleagues in the work unit and others in a functional department limited to their own discipline. Where a "vertical" department (differentiated by profession) exists in a complex organization, top people in a particular discipline are in a position to extend protection to their brother practitioners at the team level.

We have suggested that organizations largely composed of interdisciplinary teams as the basic operating unit may have distinctive characteristics. As is happens, the only studies touching upon this topic have to do with hospitals, where the structure of course is exceedingly complex and in many ways, perhaps, in a class by itself.

Little is available by way of specifically team-related studies of the position of the individual professional worker as an organization man, though the more general subject has been explored at some length. Also moderately well documented, but likewise with little reference to interdisciplinary teams, are the implications of common professional identity shared by workers, supervisors and executives or administrators.

The division of policy-making authority between team and complex organization is a matter gone over lightly, if it is touched on at all, in most reports. Whether spheres of interest are commonly mapped out, indeed whether there is any agreement defining who is to decide what, remains an unanswered question in most of the empirical studies. Even the elemental consideration of the overall body's assessment of team efficiency remains substantially unexplored.

Most descriptions of interdisciplinary team practice, both empirical and speculative, simply locate the team in a practice setting and move on to strictly team concerns. The special maintenance needs of teams, if any, and the range of staff services provided specifically to team must be intensively studied if we are to piece out any comprehensive picture. Few who have written about interdisciplinary teams have concerned themselves with the community relations problems of the group as an administrative unit; small wonder that no information has been developed comparing services provided in this connection by host agencies of various types to their interdisciplinary components.

We cannot overemphasize the importance of studying institutions with reference to common formal attributes rather than the field of practice as such. The key question is How do different types of teams, in different types of host settings, respond to typical organizational stress and crisis? Which administrative patterns of formal organization are most conducive to effective work in interdisciplinary teams? Do certain kinds of interdisciplinary teams operate more effectively under the aegis of complex organizations with specified formal characteristics? What social conditions must be defined, policy-wise, if the team is to survive and get the job done?

Empirical studies should ultimately help establish which combinations of team and host agency structure best meet the pragmatic test. The "oak tree" model of multiple subordination in decision-making suggests that superordinate controls and traditional bureaucratic models of authority are not the only viable designs for internal organization and control. The team practicing under complex organization auspices commonly lives with a large measure of inner freedom. But it is, at least potentially, subject to assessment by the larger organization; it lives by virtue of service and custodial functions provided by the organization; it may in time of crisis be sheltered behind the facade of the organization.

Selected References

Barber, Bernard C.: Problems in the sociology of the professions. Daedalus, 92:669, 1963.

Blau, Peter M.: Social integration, social ranks, and processes of interaction. Human Organization, 18:152, 1959-1960.

Blum, Richard H., and Downing, Joseph H.: Staff response to innovation in a mental health service. Amer J Public Health, 54:1230, 1964.

Fairweather, George W. (Ed.): Social Psychology in Treating Mental Illness. New York, Wiley, 1964.

Henry, Jules: Types of institutional structure. Psychiatry, 20:47, 1957.

Peck, Harris, et al: A New Pattern for Mental Health Services in a Children's Court. Springfield, Thomas, 1958.

Perrow, Charles: Hospitals: technology, structure and goals. In March, James (Ed.): Handbook of Organizations. Chicago, Rand McNally, 1965.

Stogdill, Ralph M.: Leadership, membership and organization. Psychol Bull, 47, 1950.

Thomas, Herbert E.: The dynamics of the interdisciplinary team in the adult correctional process. The Prison Journal, 44, 1964.

Chapter VI

PROFESSIONALISM, PROFESSIONALIZATION AND THE INTERDISCIPLINARY TEAM

STUDYING the nature and characteristics of interdisciplinary teams clearly necessitates some reexamination of diverse conceptions of professions and professionalism. Some aspects of interdisciplinary team practice raise questions about well-established ideas concerning the particular group of occupations in the helping professions.

Team practice, to a psychologist, may suggest reporting, interpreting, recommending; to a social worker the mere opportunity to make a colleague's services available to clients may in itself be enough to justify a commitment to team practice. A physician may envision himself in the midst of a group of ancillary personnel — a nurse, an occupational therapist, a dietician — whose professional activities simply involve the filling of his prescriptions. These "para-medical" practitioners may concur, or they may maintain that their identity as professionals requires that they exercise clinical judgment and discretion, each conceiving of the doctor's prescription not as an order but as an orientation.

Expertness and Specialization

In a sense, attainment of expertness is at the price of a fragmentation of knowledge; not uncommonly, both the members and the captain of the team lack a unifying perspective, some grasp of their common problems that transcends the specialized interests of each separate discipline. Yet the exigencies of interdisciplinary team practice impel the professional to undertake the hazardous enterprise of acquiring a measure of working familiarity with the several areas of special competence staked out as the particular preserve of each of his colleagues: the thrust is in the direction of unity if the several component efforts are to be ensured any meaning at all.

Etiquette may impel colleagues to accept the diagnostic conclusions a clinical psychologist has inferred from the behavior samples observed in interview-and-testing sessions. But some essential understanding of his diagnostic techniques in their pertinence to the group's global concerns is needed if they are to evoke the psychologist's maximum contribution. And only such an understanding can ensure their achieving a really penetrating appreciation of his insights.

Movement merely in the direction of a synthesizing grasp of the entire range of the team's activities should not be taken as symbolizing acceptance of the contention that all professionals are equally able, much less that differences in expertness are unimportant. In those fields where interdisciplinary teams are most prevalent, strong ideological bonds quite commonly link colleagues whose task activities on the job clearly stem from divergent occupational traditions. The "dynamically oriented" psychiatrist in this respect often has more in common with clinical psychologists and social workers than with physicians in other specialities. The same may be said of the physiatrist's community with the occupational therapist dedicated to a philosophy of rehabilitation, or the public health nurse's joint crusade with the public health educator.

Experts have a tendency to become so preoccupied with their own speciality that they lose perspective on the rest of the world and forget that there is more than one path to understanding. Practice as a member of an interdisciplinary team subjects the professional person to some measure of counterbalance, but by his very language the specialist tends to confine the range of his thought within the borders of the particular system with which his own competence is identified. The extent to which any particular worker's outlook becomes more catholic is dependent not only upon processes of interdisciplinary collaboration within the group, but also on his own work history and his own conceptions of the mission of the professional.

The practicing professional today recognizes that a pooling of efforts and a comprehensive perspective still leave each specialist obliged to master a wealth of detail in his own field. A concern for the place of his own expertise in the scheme of things at large impels each contributor to cultivate his own particular sector of the domain as well.

Circumstances of interdisciplinary collaboration, however, often impel well-established professions to reexamine traditional proscriptions against outsiders engaging in specified activities related to the core of professional practice, yet not necessarily unique and essential to one field alone. In health services, for example, it is only very recently that the mystique surrounding the administration of injections has been dispelled sufficiently to permit successively lower-status workers to assume responsibility. And among lawyers, debate still rages about such contentions as that of former U.S. Attorney General Nicholas J. Katzenbach that legal advice is a "job too big . . . to be left only to lawyers." American Bar Association Canon number 47, which enjoins lawyers not to aid in any way laymen engaged in "the unauthorized practice of law," still has many staunch and literalist defenders in the profession, yet there can be no denying the fact that the art of advocacy is practiced by nonlawyers as well as members of the bar.

Along with the trend toward specialization in the past few decades there has likewise clearly been a tendency to identify a growing number of traditional tasks as not requiring the attention of workers in the most highly skilled disciplines. The interdisciplinary team practice situation, making clearly visible the related skills of workers in different disciplines, has probably facilitated this "job dilution." Insofar as it has promoted fragmentation, however, it may have contributed to increased demands for nonprofessional "generalists" as well.

While the growth of interdisciplinary team practice increases the likelihood that segmental skills of specialist workers will be effectively deployed, interest in the value of a new kind of broad-spectrum innovator is likewise perceptible. Wayne Yeager and his associates have reported the development of a corps of more than two dozen college or nursing school graduates serving the Florida State Board of Health in "The Mental Health Worker: A New Public Health Professional." They contend that:

Graduates in the professional disciplines are often indoctrinated with
the sense of there-is-only-one-best-way-to-get-things-done. Also pride
of professional status may block the giving of services which are
considered beneath the dignity of the expert ... [serving in an
advisory and assisting capacity]. The mental health worker has been
able to supplement the work of the mental health professionals
without encroaching upon their fields.

In "child health conferences" where public health nurses
usually provide the greater measure of preventive and educational
services, physicians are typically invested with primary
responsibility. From a questionnaire distributed to over two
hundred workers in nine California health departments, Siegel,
Dillehay and Fitzgerald learned that three nurses out of five, and
four senior nurses out of five, favored nurses assuming primary
responsibility. But among the physicians, the sentiment ran close
to two-to-one against. It is important, however, to recognize that
among professional people who may be reluctant to relinquish the
position of preeminence there are nonetheless many who are
willing to re-think the division of labor. Where "task performance"
only is at stake, and no reassessment of "status" is implicit, feeling
is less likely to run high.

Professionalization

In the last analysis, it is the esteem of the general public that
confirms the culmination of an occupational group's endeavor to
establish itself as "professional." Discussions of the
professionalization process, however, note that a systematic
scrutiny of the operations performed by senior personnel often
results in a proliferation of subprofessional and technical
occupations about a traditionally recognized professional core. Of
course, there is room for debate about the essential characteristics
of the professions; Howard Becker is not without supporters when
he contends that the honorific title really symbolizes little more
than success in a political manipulation of the labor market.

Certain "professionalizing" occupations may profit by reflected
prestige from an already-accepted profession with which they are
associated in the public's view. But the new effect of
interdisciplinary team relationships upon the professionalization

process remains to be carefully investigated. Some work settings afford members of upwardly mobile occupational groups, whose professionalization has not progressed very far, ample opportunity to clarify their aspirations and proceed with the cultivation of crucial skills, attitudes and knowledge. The precise extent to which the prevalence of interdisciplinary teamwork in fact contributes to an occupation's becoming a profession may be difficult to assess, but a study of recent history in the field of rehabilitation might well illustrate the relationship. Certainly pervasive reference to professionalism and professionalization in rehab settings has salience to occupational trends and practices which come to the attention of any observer.

Upwardly mobile occupations, it appears, may be classified into two groups. First there are those that attain an increasing measure of autonomy and an identity ultimately unshadowed by imputations of remaining in an "ancillary" position. In the case of a second group of occupations, however, close relationships with members of established professions in interdisciplinary teams may militate against their achieving that critical measure of independence which is associated with a group's being perceived as in some capacities unique. A claim to uniqueness, it often seems, is an indispensable step in the rocky climb toward professional independence.*

In interdisciplinary team operations, the exigencies of day-to-day practice for members of a small group reinforce constraints by the several members' own professional ethical codes. This is not to say that team practice renders value conflicts and dilemmas less likely; but members are impelled by the setting to reconcile diverse ethical systems in the very process of the coordination of their endeavors. The working conditions may bring standards and values under continual scrutiny to a greater extent than is the case in individual practice. Qualitatively, the scrutiny is likely to be more broadly ranging than would be the

*Yet occupational identity by reason of unique skills will in itself, not suffice for achievement of professional identity. Witness the experience of prosthetists, who may be barred from the fraternity of professions because the occupation is so largely focussed about manual rather than verbal skills, and relatively so wanting in theoretic undergirding.

case were all discussants private practitioners of the same discipline and essentially similar education. However, professional authority, in the last analysis, stems neither from schools nor from certificating bodies, neither from complex organizations nor from teams. As Arthur Brayfield, Executive Officer of the American Psychological Association recently put it, professionals ultimately are answerable "to the society which accords us special privilege and expects from us special responsibility."

The Client

We have not examined the position of the consumer of team services — the client — thus far, since it is team structure and team processes with which we are primarily concerned. Nonetheless, those professional people like other workers who provide services, justify their labor as meeting social needs. A rationale of team practice therefore must ultimately consider whether clients are served, and how well. The assumption is that clients will find that teams can provide better services than individual professionals. But, this is largely an assumption; there have been few endeavors to put the proposition to a pragmatic test.

Client demands for services which the practitioner is ethically enjoined from providing, raise a dilemma familiar to the student of professions. In team practice, however, there is the additional conflict between client needs which the professional is pledged to meet and bureaucratic rules which may stultify the development of individualized relationships. Mere access to the team may be denied entirely on the basis of some intake priorities scheme. With a more refined division of labor and a greater likelihood that numbers of adjunctive specialists will participate in processes of help and care, persons receiving services must revise certain of their expectations or cope with disappointment. It may become necessary to accept some measure of relationship with a number of professionals, rather than establish a firm bond with one only. The intensity of the link between helper and helped may be attenuated. In any event, the client's sharing of confidences with his helper must take account of the omnipresent colleagues — unless, of course, the client is deceived or the team practices coordinately behind a set of Chinese walls.

As the professional relationship is transformed for the interdisciplinary team practitioner, the client finds services being provided in a different interpersonal context. Little is known about clients' personal ties to teams, but the clinical literature strongly implies that it is an individual, or several individuals, rather than an association of persons that is perceived as actually helping-healing.

It is customary in certain settings, e.g., child guidance clinics, to designate a particular worker as "primary therapist" for each client, even where the case is formally thought of as being carried by the team. It would appear that this reinforcement of the treatment relationship along more traditional professional lines may throw the practitioners themselves off balance; not uncommonly both the "primary therapist" and his team colleagues come to refer to such cases as "his" or "hers."

The extent, however, to which a pattern of team structure is consonant with distinctive characteristics of clientele is virtually an unexplored problem. For example, Carter and Margolin note "the client's need and expectancy to establish a relationship with a single professional person" as affecting the tendency not to differentiate the roles of diverse professionals in mental health teams. But the question might be raised as to whether client expectancy (if not client need) may not vary with socioeconomic status and life experience with "helping and healing" professionals. People who have had bitter experiences with bureaucracies and officialdom may be slow to recognize the potential helpfulness of a complex interdisciplinary team. No matter how dignified and refined the approach, the team may have to "sell itself" to some of those most in need of its services. In any event, the attitude with which the team confronts the client epitomizes a crucial ideological concern of the professions.

Ideology

In addition to the theory that interdisciplinary collaboration results in the provision of more adequate services, two ideological main currents are perceptible in interdisciplinary team practice: the valuational philosophies of the several professions, and the various distinctive approaches to service methods and goals epitomized in specific "approaches" or schools of thought.*

Dedication to the art and a commitment to human service, more specifically to the client's welfare, are among the hallmarks of a professional. Individuals' hierarchies of professional value, however, are perceptibly different among colleagues of the same discipline. For example, there is a difference between the doctor whose primary orientation is to his colleagues, and the "individualistic type" whose concern for patients is preeminent. Similar variations in reference group may be noted among people in other professions, and these may well have a material impact upon group solidarity and allegiance in interdisciplinary teams. Moreover, conceptions of the professional relationship itself vary widely.

Psychoanalytic approaches have become so dominant in psychotherapeutic agencies that the term "dynamic" may be said to have virtually lost its comprehensive implications, being employed today almost exclusively to identify Freudians or neo-Freudians. In some teams, lively debates harking back to school days may set the more orthodox followers of Ernest Jones and Heinz Hartmann apart from practitioners who consider themselves followers of Horney, Fromm or Sullivan; and the disciples of both schools of thought may subscribe to professional principles abhorrent to a Carl Rogers enthusiast.

But as new problems come to the fore in society, some historic disputes in professional circles recede into the background. Conceivably, the pressing ideological disjunction confronting team practitioners today, is that between therapeutic services to individuals and groups on the one hand, and the cultivation of effective anticipatory and preventive modes of address to social problems on the other.† Debates generated in the poverty programs and issues arising in the black liberation movement have led to further exploration in recent years of previously

---

*The rehabilitation movement and the psychoanalytic orientation are two examples.
†At the 1966 meeting of the American Public Health Association, for example, Leonard Duhl, a psychiatrist who served as Special Assistant to the U.S. Secretary of Housing and Urban Development, declared that steps to take people out of degrading circumstances in public housing could do more for mental health than clinics.

patched-over disputes in outlook and goals among psychiatrists, psychologists and social workers.

The extent, on the other hand, to which there is an interpenetration of the distinctive techniques, theories and ideologies of different professions closely associated in team practice is a question still to be investigated. We know most about divisive processes like role bargaining and role differentiation; the ways in which groups elaborate a common understanding of the task at hand and hammer out some sort of common approach have been less amply documented. The dynamics of sharing and the areas in which professions associated in interdisciplinary team processes have the most significant and lasting influence upon one another remain relatively unexplored in actual field study. Whatever the division of labor, however, the clinical situation imposes a demand for individual judgment, over and above any practice theory which may tend to make for group solidarity.

Judgment and Skills

"Judgment" presupposes an ethical base, and judgment within the matrix of a disciplined profession implicitly is founded upon a commonly accepted system of values. The valuing process — whether undertaken jointly and at the conscious level of awareness, or intuitively in response to preconscious or unconscious standards — necessarily involves a hierarchical ranking of good and evil.

But "judgment" typically involves something more than the application of knowledge and understanding in the light of values. A willingness to accept the desirability or the necessity of acting in hazardous situations is implied. Judging commonly involves taking risks, living with the uncertainty as well as the revelation afforded by our feeble grasp of the laws of probability. And judgment involves accepting responsibility for deploying to the "best" possible effect those resources available at a given moment in time. It involves living with the awareness that both art and science want perfecting.

To accept professional responsibility, of course, also implies being willing to "refer" those problems more likely to be solved by a colleague, or to consult another when "judgment" suggests a pooling of opinion or of risk. Certain prerogatives traditionally taken unto themselves by physicians, therefore, become a recurrent source of friction in interdisciplinary team practice. Since the autonomous exercise of judgment is often identified as an integral aspect of professional identity, some workers often called "paramedical" may be jealous of prerogatives they identify as essential to their identity as professional persons.

A social worker, for example, will typically be willing to help a physician with whom he is associated tackle a problem with social as well as medical implications, but he will insist upon making his own decision as to just what social work methods and techniques ought appropriately to be employed. The accredited occupational therapist's services, contrariwise, are rendered on medical prescription only, at the direction of and in collaboration with physicians; the basic certification of these workers, in fact, is provided jointly by the American Medical Association and the American Occupational Therapy Association.

Still another approach to combined operations is implicit in an American Psychological Association 1954 statement defining psychologists' activities in their relations with other professions. Team practice involving collaborative decision-making is described there as providing "certain social controls," making it an appropriate situation for "psychologists who do not yet meet the high qualifications expected of persons for independent practice." This last, in turn, contrasts with tradition in the practice of social work, where independent (private) practice is the exception, and even the most highly regarded professionals have historically been employees in one or another institutional setting.

Interest in the creative rather than the purely remunerative aspects of the work, a hallmark of the professional, may be manifested nowhere as vigorously as among practitioners on interdisciplinary practice teams. And the controls imposed by collegial surveillance may be more rigorous in this practice situation than in any other. Certainly the likelihood of technical criticism from persons not themselves professional colleagues is nowhere else made as great as in the interdisciplinary team. Professionals whose on-the-job security is based upon the specialist's fluent command of the language of his own discipline, may be embarrassed when more broad-minded colleagues demand a catholic approach. Nonetheless, as indicated above, there is still a persistent hazard of orthodox adherence to narrow ideologies that reach across disciplinary boundaries.

Professional skill and judgment may be manifested in a wide range of behaviors, but demands made of a worker by colleagues of other disciplines will vary widely. The others may simply "expect a man to do his job" or they may quite persistently raise sophisticated questions about the "whys and wherefores" of his expert decisions. An individual joining a team as a "clinical psychologist," for example, may be expected by most of his colleagues to be capable of administering a variety of psychological tests and interpreting the results. Some of these colleagues may expect him to decide which instruments are appropriate in each clinical situation; others may believe it does not impugn the psychologist's professional judgment to ask that he employ some specifically requested question and answer techniques, rather than to ask that he try to answer some specific question. But to many psychologists, an issue of principle is at stake. Similarly, "the confidentiality principle" is a fundamental in many different professional education curriculums. But to hear a social worker contend that information he has procured in line of duty is a confidence shared with him personally, and with him alone, may come as a rude shock to professional colleagues on the team who might suppose that potentially useful information should be shared with all the helpers who are in a position to employ it to the advantage of the person who has sought help from the team.

Professional skills, in modern times, characteristically are shared. Nonetheless, shared knowledge is largely dependent not only upon free access to formal education, but also upon publication (e.g., in professional journals). Until we achieve a shared understanding of the intricacies of interdisciplinary relationships, today held as a "knack" known to the initiated and their intimates only, a fundamental element of the professional's credo will be violated. "Trade secrets" may persist by reason of a pervasive inertia and lack of alertness, they cannot be attributed to selfishness alone.

It is something of an axiom that only an expert can evaluate a fellow expert and that each profession accredits its own fraternity. Evaluation and assessment of the performance of members of a different discipline, therefore, is implicitly problematic for many team leaders or administrators. Sometimes, of course, a bit of verbal legerdemain will smooth the way, as in the case of a physician's referring to his colleagues as practicing "paramedical" disciplines. The contention that only his peers assess the expert is perhaps nowhere more commonly disproved than in the case of social workers in interdisciplinary team practice. The decision to hire, the evaluation of on going service processes and the power to promote or to terminate are all likely to be in the hands of an individual with no professional qualifications in social work.

In interdisciplinary team practice it seems that colleagues almost always impute expertness to each worker in the field with which he identifies himself. It is, however, debatable whether this implies acceptance of his conclusions and recommendations without any concern for an understanding of the underlying evidence-inference process. As we pointed out a decade ago in our book on professional education for rehabilitation workers, students (of social work, for example) should learn to couch case presentations in explicit behavioral terms, as well as conceptually. Colleagues of other disciplines may thereby more readily follow the reasoning undergirding their diagnostic contributions and appreciate the thinking that lies behind recommendations of one or another course of services.

It is not uncommon in interdisciplinary team debate for a difference in judgment between colleagues to be construed either as an attack *ad hominem* or a criticism of the particular discipline an individual represents. In teams where there is more than one member from a discipline, such a defense can elicit two sequences of events: (1) members belonging to the same discipline as the colleague whose judgment has been questioned may support his judgment as a support of their discipline — and hence, of themselves, (2) these same workers may each separately or in *ad hoc* disciplinary conference ("within the family") privately support the criticism if it appears to have technical merit. Needless to say, such behavior clearly indicates that whatever organic solidarity prevails in the team, it cannot compete with a universalistic norm guaranteeing a practitioner support from members of his own profession in the presence of "laymen" – for to such professionals, no outsider can be anything but a layman.

Role bargaining within interdisciplinary teams may find reflection in disputation between spokesmen for professional associations in the community arenas. Witness the yet-to-be-concluded effort of psychiatrists to restrict the psychotherapeutic activities of psychologists, and the contention of both social workers and vocational rehabilitation counsellors that planning the coordination of services is a, if not "the," distinctive contribution of their group.

The rationale for the interdisciplinary team, of course, is that problems in practice demand a more diversified armamentarium of skills than is possessed by any one profession. As a consequence, a measure of open-endedness is implicit in most multidisciplinary units as they are activated: if a psychiatrist does a better job with the help of a psychologist and a social worker, it is at least worth considering whether there may not also be occasion to draw upon the special knowledge of the sociologist, say, or the public health nurse. The ideology of "serving the whole man" may appear as some sort of premonition in the literature presaging the advent of interdisciplinary teams. Advocacy of ever-closer collaborative bonds has become more vigorous and widespread as interdisciplinary teams themselves have proliferated. It now seems appropriate to consider the possible contribution of any specialist whose skill is addressed to a relevant but at present unserved aspect of human need or distress. Furthermore, new occupations have achieved a measure of status and are on the road to becoming recognized as professional in the light of their undoubted contributions to multidisciplinary team practice. The physiotherapist, the rehabilitation counsellor, the speech therapist and, perhaps, the prosthetist belong in this category. And indigenous workers recruited among client groups of the poverty programs promise to bring to the interdisciplinary pool new resources of insight and more fluent access to people in need.

The traditional sense of obligation the individual professional person felt toward his client has been somewhat modified with the bureaucratization of practice. Yet the employee of an organization of national stature may be insulated against some of the parochial pressures which can threaten the integrity of the individual practitioner. Being "just another employee" among many people comprising a highly complex work force may in fact afford the professional worker a special freedom. And as an employee, he may find himself able to engage in the most highly specialized practice, an opportunity open only to the exceptionally gifted among private practitioners.

Accrediting Bodies and Reference Groups

We have discussed as reference group behavior the ways in which practitioners model their activity according to what they believe to be the standards accepted by groups to whose judgment they defer. But this endeavor to conform to social expectations is not limited to individuals. Interdisciplinary teams as groups are responsive to pressure and jointly strive to keep oriented to the thrust of diverse demands from power centers within the organization and in the larger community without. Orienting a mental hospital service to the concerns underlying "the therapeutic community," for example, is likely to involve reassuring nurses that new ways of doing the job are approved by the leaders of their profession as well as the charge nurses and the medical director. Furthermore, personnel of all disciplines involved may discover that the understanding and good will of such local authorities as the police are important, too. A treatment institution cannot operate as an island entire unto itself; commonly accepted social values impinge upon life within the walls, as well as without.

The work group and its members are likely to have recurrent contacts with agencies in the community providing other services to team clients, or studying and planning around social problems with which the team itself is concerned. While the team may contribute to the work of other agencies and to planning processes in the community, it also is affected by community practices and policy pressures. Yet the operating unit is not altogether free to decide on its own which clients will receive which services. It may respond to the expectations it imputes to one or another audience with which it communicates. But, as we have indicated above, there are several kinds of authority affecting the actions of a team. A court clinic, for example, must operate within the societally determined structure of law as well as the particular administrative structure of its court. And team practice in a nursery school may have to link in with licensing regulations of the state as well as the child care and child development beliefs of a particular culture, or subculture, at a particular moment in time.

Accrediting organizations as well as standard-setting groups that do not formally accredit, exert a substantial influence not only upon complex organizations in which teams practice, but upon the teams themselves. Both the team and its several members order their conduct to the expectations of society in general and, more particularly, to what they believe are the expectations of groups whose opinion or whose power they respect. It is by no means inconceivable, for example, that in a professional forum a mental health team in a court clinic might undertake to advocate a theory of its mission and the law's mandate to the court rather clearly at variance with the philosophy of the presiding judge. The distribution of power in the society, however, being what it is, it is unlikely the team would undertake such a debate in a purely civic forum, unless it had the stout support of a citizens' lobby lined up beforehand.

Along with some attenuation of his direct personal relationship to the client, the professional person finds that interdisciplinary team practice alters his social situation by implicating him in responsibilities to the team as a group, to its leader (if it has one) and to the complex organization in which it is lodged. It would seem that the profession as such, and his professional associations, may loom larger in the work life of the interdisciplinary team worker than in the case with his brethren practicing in a less "diluted" milieu. As a reference group, the profession is an audience with which each practitioner communicates; it comes close to being the ultimate source of authority. The profession implicitly affords each practitioner guidelines and examples with which he can compare work demands made upon him, as well as his own behavior. Moreover, the very existence of the profession as a social entity provides some potential leverage to members who find themselves in a bind where interdisciplinary relationships unfold in a bizarre fashion.

Eric Ashby, Master of Cambridge's Clare College, has observed that a professor's esteem on campus is largely a reflection of his reputation among professional colleagues elsewhere. The same relationship seems to prevail with reference to the ultimate source of status rewards which a team, or perhaps even more commonly, a sponsoring agency confers upon a worker. Even his self-esteem is founded upon peer acceptance. Small wonder that reference group processes are so consequential, and that extramural reference groups must figure so significantly in studies of the internal dynamics of interdisciplinary teams.

Work settings affording an opportunity to become acquainted with interdisciplinary practice are sought after by educators planning internships, field instruction experiences and practicums. The schools and the team influence one another, though the patterning of influence will depend upon the character and extent of consultative services provided by academic faculty as well as the demands that may be made of regular staff for preceptorial sessions. This dialogue between field and classroom magnifies the shadow that team practitioners cast on the professional scene. As a result, opportunities to serve as a field instructor or supervisor constitute an inducement in recruitment of team personnel; to be regarded as qualified for such work apparently enhances the self-image of the practitioner.

Some Historical Perspectives

Looked upon as a factor in historical process, interdisciplinary team practice may be related to a number of long-range trends in the occupational field. Over the years the public has tended to limit permission to engage in specified kinds of work. Licensing and similar regulation stipulates the qualifications of those who may undertake to heal the sick, just as it restricts the self-qualified from simply representing that they can repair plumbing or design houses.* Along with the license, most professional associations

---

*Note in this connection the recent rash of legislation to specify who may practice, for example, psychotherapy. Since it may be merely the name rather than the work that is licensed, laws also stipulate who may refer to himself by some restricted job title, e.g., "social worker." Licensing, of coures, is no novelty, but the considerable increase during the past fifty years in the number of licensed occupations is noteworthy.

affirm that they have a mandate to define the limits of what is right and proper with respect to their field of work, not only for their own members but for every prospective practitioner as well. Both license and mandate tend to be implemented under conditions of interdisciplinary team practice in ways which are fraught with hazard of jealous conflict among the occupational groups involved. Nonetheless, the juvenile court judge, for example, consults with nonjudicial colleagues before making a disposition (sentencing) rather more freely and more frequently than other judges do. In a child guidance clinic, the psychiatrist's mandate to take legal responsibility for diagnosis and treatment is frequently watered down in the exigencies of a busy practice schedule to something approximating a *pro forma* certification of that large proportion of the caseload which is principally carried by colleagues from other disciplines. In both instances, a shift from traditional definition of the content of professional practice is attributable to a cumulating sense of the value of team engagement. It should by now be a commonplace to note that the practice of modern scientific medicine requires not only an ample armamentarium of highly expensive machines, but also a complex of social organization and the skills of colleagues often identified as being in "paramedical" occupations.

Professional workers who want to avoid uneconomical employment of their time may be interested in any setup which will enable them to maximize the proportion of the work day they can actually devote to tasks at their highest level of skill. Newer conceptions of community medical planning, for example, have projected hospital programs reaching beyond the institution's walls into homes of the sick and the neighborhood at large. A generation ago, specialization was the "coming thing." The ethical professional was learning to stick to the work he knew best, and to refer the remaining problems to specialists in allied disciplines. Today, team operations make it possible for even broadly skilled workers to refer and to consult on cases, since adjunctive resources have been built right into the practice situation.

In many settings, it is no longer up to a single worker to decide how the diverse skills and energies of the whole group will be deployed; the colleagues collectively carry the responsibility for deciding. By the same token, process segmentation makes it possible for a worker to be relieved of the obligation to perform tasks really peripheral to his essential expertness: a physician, for example, can rely upon a social worker's specialized knowledge of community resources when patient treatment approaches an "after care" phase. In team settings, tasks otherwise neglected as unnecessary or unimportant or too clumsy to arrange on an *ad hoc* basis are undertaken routinely. A means has been evolved for the almost routine family visit to amplify understanding of a patient's situation, or the almost routine psychological testing session to compare a patient's behavior against standards of performance set by a rather sizeable number of his peers.

The small-scale unit of employment, once typical of the professions, seems a little less typical with each passing year. And the professionals most commonly included in interdisciplinary teams are salaried workers, almost exclusively. Entrepreneurial aspects of the professional occupations go into almost total eclipse in the interdisciplinary team sector.* Income, we might note, is regarded as a distinctly secondary motivation in conceptualizing the ideal professional man, and he may be assumed to be interested in money more as a means to facilitate his serving function rather than as an end in itself. It would appear that interdisciplinary teamworkers in many disciplines have lower incomes than colleagues in the same occupation not practicing in teams.

If the situation of the professional man in the interdisciplinary team differs economically from that of some of his brethren, it is distinctive also in that numbers of behavioral scientists are associated with, if not participating in, these new teams. Furthermore, one numerous and strategic group, the clinical psychologists, have been schooled in a discipline where scientific values and concerns were stressed at least as much as the professional. And those whose education has been primarily scientific rather than professional, sometimes find themselves "in a bind" when they believe they must choose between the service ideal and a quest for truth.

---

*There probably are a few interdisciplinary teams in the labor market as private practice groups. But some nonprofit institutions allow professional employees free time for private practice.

An academic discipline stresses theoretical research, while a profession stresses goal-directed practice. There clearly are differences between the self-image of the scientist and that of the professional: a lawyer's interest in a case, for example, centers on his efforts to reach a decision on the issues and not upon scientific explanation. The movement to broaden legal aid to the poor and to bring poor people into friendlier relationships with the law is involving lawyers — previously, perhaps, the most independent of professionals — in interdependent practice relationships. And newer conceptions of advocacy as an aspect of professional practice are coloring the task content in other occupations — social work, in particular.

Team settings, in any event, are employing increasing numbers of professional workers and there has been a noteworthy trend toward the professionalization of workers in subprofessional and semiprofessional fields. Rehabilitation during the past two decades has provided a good example, and it may be that such current developments as "the war on poverty" presage a cultivation of the social welfare field along similar lines. Certainly the trend toward involving increasing numbers of semiprofessional and nonprofessional recruits from among the populations served, presages the development of new occupations and new team relationships among those concerned with helping the poor.

Shifts in Traditional Status and Career Patterns

In a number of professions, the cultivation of expertness has both created a need for interdisciplinary teamwork and the manpower to staff the teams. But experts come to the team setting with professional self-images which may generate sharp conflicts in "mixed company" regardless of their acceptance in the midst of the professional family. Professor A's traditional self-image may incorporate presumptions that any team operation wants a captain and that the captain should be an A-worker; Dr. B, on the other hand, may stand firm on a conception of a distinctive expertness, a uniqueness which merits the claim of equal status with any and all, an essential quality which justifies insistence that truly professional collaborative practice cannot be sustained except among teammates who relate to one another as equals.

Philosophical disquisitions on interprofessional relationships are replete with admonitions to live and let live. Nonetheless, competition among professions is, in fact, a rather basic aspect of their orientation. Interdisciplinary team practice and the move into the inner councils of complex organizations has perhaps affected the nature of some points of contention, but the contention itself has persisted. There can be no disputing the fact that activities in one or another profession perennially are found to overlap the legal or traditional preserve of some sister vocation. And where practitioners of diverse callings collaborate in the activities of an interdisciplinary team, one worker or another may take upon himself the responsibility of "orienting" colleagues of different professions according to what he conceives to be the practice mandate assumed by his own. In recent years, for example, social workers have been the center of some contention arising out of the broadening concern of other professionals with problems of poverty.

Sizeable federal outlays addressed to problems conceptualized as having to do with psychopathology have contributed to a sharpening of a number of conflicts between those doctors who are psychiatrists, and nonphysicians whose doctorates are in psychology rather than medicine. Delineating the role of the psychologist under new federal legislation for comprehensive community mental health centers, Yolles, a psychiatrist, points out that

> Leadership is based upon individual competence, and not upon membership in a particular discipline ... The federal regulations ... provided that a qualified psychiatrist will be responsible for the clinical program ... Nowhere is it suggested that administrative leadership be limited to psychiatrists.

He did not indicate what proportion of the new centers availing themselves of the latitude of the regulations described had psychiatrists as administrators and what proportion in fact had nonpsychiatrists as leaders.

Just as established differentials in status have come under fire, there has likewise been a shift in the stereotyped notion of a career. Traditionally, this has been thought to proceed from a beginner's grade in a chosen profession to some final pinnacle of excellence and proficiency. Practitioners in interdisciplinary teams almost without exception occupy statuses which are "determinate;" entry requirements are formal and elaborately prescribed, and there usually is an expectation that role performance will be within narrow and definite limits.* Career considerations are very much to the fore and the achievements of higher-echelon certifications may prove a powerful recruitment incentive. There are advantages and preferments, too, which accrue to workers who broaden their skills in meeting novel demands of practice. Professional workers in interdisciplinary team practice may have moved into such positions at any of three rather different points in their careers: (1) team practice may be the very first work undertaken by the neophyte upon completion of his professional education, (2) a position may be filled by a "seasoned" worker, well established in the profession, broadening the base of his professional experience, or (3) team practice may come as the capstone, the culmination of a career.

The long-range implications of an increase in the number of employed professionals who are employees could be better understood if more was known about the age groups into which "free" professionals fall, and the nature of circumstances which discourage young professionals today from entering upon independent practice at the outset of their careers. In any event, a more thorough canvass of the characteristics of interdisciplinary team practice should include an exploration of the hypothesis that it is differentially attractive to professionals according to age: we suggest a bimodal distribution of young persons evolving a career along newer lines, and workers going into interdisciplinary team practice after a ten to twenty year "seasoning" period.†

The pattern, however, varies from profession to profession, with some (social work, for example) rather discouraging team practice at the outset of the career, while others (clinical psychology, for

---

*The expectation, as we have indicated above, often is at variance with realities of interdisciplinary team practice.

†Bimodality is probably more characteristic of interdisciplinary team practitioners in particular professions, e.g., social work, physical therapy.

example) prepare the certificated beginner to meet team responsibilities without any "seasoning" beyond the internship indicated. Among probation officers, on the other hand, any considerable involvement in multidisciplinary consultations beyond merely reporting to a judge may be expected only of workers with years of experience buttressed by a professional curriculum undertaken late in the career. In addition, or alternatively, bright professionally educated neophytes may be assigned such responsibilities, especially where the probation department includes cohorts with different levels of professionalization.

In the case of some workers, e.g., physicians, engagement in interdisciplinary team practice usually involves choosing a salaried position, a departure, albeit an increasingly common one, from the traditional economic status of the "free" professions. For the social worker, on the other hand, no such question arises; the profession from its beginnings has involved acceptance of employee status and practice as a representative of an organization. Furthermore, interdisciplinary practice is a common incident in his professional orientation and career.

Team practitioners appear to constitute a special subgroup within each profession; they are not quite "typical" nor usually a part of a majority subculture. Whether workers on interdisciplinary teams and professionals focally concerned with interdisciplinary team problems constitute identifiable subelites in the various professional fields is obscure; journal publication, programming at professional meetings and certain developments in professional associations point in that direction. In each profession, the elite includes members identified with interdisciplinary team practice and education for interdisciplinary teamwork; however, interdisciplinary team people nowhere comprise the entire elite of a profession. The relative esteem in which interdisciplinary team leaders are held and the influence they wield among their professional peers varies widely, as does the articulateness and commitment of noninterdisciplinary or antiinterdisciplinary leaders in professional groups. The nature and extent of interdisciplinary team impact in various professional associations and the reasons (historical and otherwise) for differences are matters to which researchers might well turn attention.

Distinctive characteristics of interdisciplinary team practice settings may complement developing trends within a particular profession. Thus demands that teamworkers have no conflicting responsibilities to seniors outside the team take on a very special meaning in a profession such as social work, where a long-term trend toward a loosening of intraprofessional supervisory bonds is becoming increasingly apparent.

A partial listing of the variety of attractions that may impel a professional person not to choose independent practice reads like a description of the nature of interdisciplinary teamwork: continual stimulating debate, opportunity for superspecialization and less pressures for certain kinds of conformity. We might note in this last connection that the individual interdisciplinary teamworker not uncommonly can derive the advantages of association with a sizeable number of colleagues and an agency which is a fixture of a community while himself remaining "one of a kind," the sole representative of his own profession on the team.

While, according to knowledgeable observers, employment in organizational settings is increasingly characteristic of today's professional man, little attention has been turned to the extent of interdisciplinary team practice among professionals. While we cannot say what proportion of professionals who are employees are in interdisciplinary teams, even a passing acquaintance with interdisciplinary team practice suggests that the overwhelming majority of professional workers who are in interdisciplinary teams are neither freely associated independent practitioners nor employees of the team itself.

The proliferation of interdisciplinary team practice is associated with increases in the employment of professional people by large enterprises. But the large enterprises in which the preponderant majority of interdisciplinary team professional workers are employed are in the public service sector of the economy (governmental and philanthropic). Such increases as have occurred in the number of interdisciplinary team workers, therefore, are not substantially related to increases in the employment of professionals by business enterprises.

Interdisciplinary teams are a well-established practice pattern in mental hospitals, child guidance clinics and county public health departments. During the past two decades, this staffing pattern has been doctrinally ensconced in the rehabilitation field, and it figures increasingly in discussion of operations in the social courts as well. Dozens of interdisciplinary teams have been set up to perform routine diagnostic screenings in connection with aid to the disabled programs under social security and the several hundred community mental health centers now being established are subject to federal regulations clearly pointed in the direction of interdisciplinary team practice. The "total push" programs characteristic of the "war on poverty" tend to generate a variety of relatively stable interdisciplinary collaborations, and though the picture is at present by no means clear, some of the discussions of legal aid, consumer counselling and citizen's advice projects clearly look to interdisciplinary team approaches to the public service process. Moreover, recruitment and other literature for the professions associated with medicine not infrequently allude to the attractions of collaborative practice.

While there appears to be an increasing tendency for workers to be recruited for interdisciplinary team positions immediately upon completion of professional education, the literature on the subject stresses the need for mature, sophisticated, highly experienced people. Whether interdisciplinary team practice in fact represents the foundation of a career, a way stage or the capstone is a question yet to be investigated. Most probably, the career pattern typical of one profession will be found to differ, at least somewhat, from patterns typical of others.

The interdisciplinary team situation affects various practitioners' personal aspirations and their striving to achieve individual goals. Typically, there is no upward mobility opportunity "built into" practice positions on an interdisciplinary team; except for workers who become captains, promotion involves leaving the team. A common incentive, however, is the chance of becoming involved in the supervision of students, since team settings are frequently employed by professional schools for field instruction. Opportunities for prestigious, even lucrative, part-time employment on the faculty of a professional school are likewise not uncommonly attached to team practice openings. These "fringe benefits" prove compatible with the ambitions of some, just as the intrinsic fascination of challenges to professional imagination preoccupy others.

An increasing number of newly qualified workers in certain fields, e.g., public health and corrections, have been provided substantial orientation to interdisciplinary teamwork thanks to federal stipends to professional students and federal subvention of both academic and field instructors. While it remains to be seen how many interdisciplinary team-oriented graduates will continue in such practice over the years, federally financed and federally supported programs routinely staffed by interdisciplinary teams have been expanding continuously in the past decade or two. And funds made available subject to very liberal postgraduation commitment have helped to acquaint promising candidates in a number of fields with attractive new practice opportunities of an interdisciplinary team character.

The long-range impact of these "aid to education" programs upon the competitive market for professional school graduates is a topic eminently deserving exploration not only by educators and economists, but by students in the professional schools themselves. In moving to ensure appropriate staffing of programs to which the Congress attached highest priority, the Government has materially influenced the content and outcome of professional education across the country. The influence was exerted in a collaborative process involving professional schools, faculty spokesman, government officials and university administrators, as well as leading figures in professional associations and practice agencies. The fact that there was broad-gauge joint planning cannot gainsay the continuing curricular impact and the consequent impact upon the labor market of a monumental effort to guarantee future staffing of rehabilitation agencies, veteran's hospitals, community mental health centers, etc. The public interest, beyond a doubt, has been served by these innovations, but the likelihood is that they will lead to a smaller proportion of new graduates entering private practice, a larger proportion heading for team settings.

Learning about Teamwork in the
Professional School

Those responsible for the education of professional people commonly view their task as related to a student's lifetime career. It therefore is not today's practice, or even tomorrow's only, with which they will be concerned. Phenomena such as interdisciplinary team practice challenge the educators to predict the future. In the long view, is this an upcoming element that will be basic in future practice, or merely a fad meriting scant concern? If a subject passes muster as sufficiently important to claim attention in competition with others, three curriculum decisions must be made: (1) what specifically are the educators' "objectives," (2) what "content" must be taught, (3) what pedagogical "methods" are likeliest to lead to the desired learning.

In recent years, increasing attention has been turned to the part professional schools can play in preparing graduates for interdisciplinary team practice. Planning education implies an awareness on the part of the teacher of what changes he is expecting in his students. These changes, of course, include new attitudes as well as new skills and the knowledge essential to skill employment. Preparation for interdisciplinary team practice requires clarification of expectations, orientation to distinctive aspects of subcultural values and organization practices, maximizing the interpersonal skills of workers in their relationships with colleagues, as well as those with clients.

Educators are aware of the fact that "transfer of learning" is likeliest if there is teaching particularly oriented to transfer. In professional education, particularly where learning takes place in some unique field setting, it is crucial that the instructor endeavor to orient the student to aspects of the setting which are typical of all other settings in the same class. But the alert and sophisticated instructor can teach a general lesson in organizational analysis at the same time he is helping the student learn how to get along in a specific subculture. There are certain survival skills generally applicable to all interdisciplinary team situations.

We have pointed out elsewhere that the professional person must not only have a clear idea of his role, but a willingness to redefine it in the give-and-take of interdisciplinary debate. The educator of future professionals must assume the responsibility for engendering both the will and the skill in his students.

Preparing students for tomorrow's practice, and for practice the day after tomorrow, professional schools perennially come into conflict with some in the professional establishment who favor greater stress on today's knowledge, or even on what yesterday was believed to be best.* However pervasive this probelm may be with regard to other curricular areas, there can be no doubt that it occasions spirited debate when the teaching of interprofessional relationships and interdisciplinary team practice is reviewed by peers. Formal evaluation of schools may be turned over to the vanguard element of a profession, and education with an eye to the future may be endorsed. But among rank-and-file practitioners, and middle-echelon people who employ or supervise the newly graduated, the tide of opinion may run strong to "the old way, the good way." Criticism of the new generation of nurses, of the "new look" in social work, clearly suggests attitudes ambivalent, to say the least, toward abandoning traditional images of the "handmaiden."

If intraprofessional differences of view about role models constitute a dilemma for curriculum planners, the same may be said of interprofessional disparities in criteria of credibility. Each profession attaches its own weighted importance to diverse learning situations: the laboratory, the library, the classroom and the field. And out of his own experience, in the light of his teacher's manifested values, the graduate evolves his own attitudes toward different sources of knowledge. Some interdisciplinary team professionals who are very much concerned with practice rather than scientific problems, nonetheless quite commonly may be found organizing their behavior around norms and a self-image primarily reflecting the values and aspirations not of service but of research.†

---

*Any calling that thinks of itself as a profession can adapt the motto of the law school professor "The mission is not to produce lawyers but minds trained for law."

†And even in medical schools, where the service ideal is well-entrenched, thinking about interdisciplinary relationships in treatment still is dominated by traditional hierarchical

Pioneer educators in a number of disciplines have stressed the importance of preparing for interdisciplinary team practice in the basic professional curriculum, and the indispensability of learning opportunities in field settings where neophytes can be prepared alongside colleagues in other professions who are themselves students. If the future professional's very first practice responsibilities are undertaken in surroundings pervaded by interdisciplinary sharing and interchange, it may be less likely that he will make a later appearance among fully qualified practitioners in his field unacquainted with the scope and depth of sister disciplines and lacking in respect for the knowledge, skills and dedication of colleagues. It follows that instructors in field settings must themselves be personally committed to the central value of collaborative practice; they must themselves demonstrate from day-to-day a thoroughgoing respect for the expertise as well as the contribution of colleagues in other fields.

In addition to cultivating a familiarity with other professions and with the division of labor in practice settings, those preparing professional students for interdisciplinary team practice clearly must be concerned with enhancing technical competence in elements of small group process. Most educators would probably also stress the importance of professional values in defining team

values. Among such technically progressive professionals as chairman of departments of preventive medicine, a clear majority just a few years ago were reported envisioning the practice of the future as being carried on by teams headed by physicans. Many, furthermore, envisioned medicine as being practice by doctors, with members of related professions identified as helpers only.

More recently, plans of the Association of American Medical Colleges envisioned curriculums including practice experience as a member of a collaborative team. But traditional claims to superior status persist, and the same document that advocated an increase in the number of cooperating nonphysicians referred to "tasks that might be performed just as well and at substantially lower cost by less thoroughly trained persons." Apparently the only nonphysicians invited to join team operations were thought of as inherently less thoroughly prepared than their medical colleagues.

Medicine is the professional discipline where the rationale for specialist expertness has perhaps come to be most deeply entrenched. It therefore seems reasonable to expect that physicians learn, as a part of their basic education, that there are medico-social problems, for example, likely to require more than the humane sympathies of a general practitioner manipulating the patient-physician relationship. The quandary of the girl pregnant but unwed is a case in point: Understanding the desirability of enlisting the collaborated skills of a responsible interdisciplinary team specializing in cases of this sort might well be an objective worth considering in medical education.

goals, since mastering technique in group dynamics potentially improves the learner's ability simply to manipulate others in the service of a great diversity of possible organizational objectives. The professional perspective on task performance implies that the social desirability of the ends sought be valued above technical proficiency itself; he who acquires the capacity to manipulate must discipline his potential power to abuse, as well.

Preparation for optimal effectiveness in interdisciplinary team practice would therefore appear first of all to require a presentation of pooled (as distinguished from "unidisciplinary") efforts as a fundamental during the aspirant's period of becoming identified with his profession. This means learning from personal experience (not precept alone) to value the distinctive expertness of sister disciplines. It means becoming conversant with some common terminological and even theoretical foundations alongside beginners in disciplines with which there may subsequently be associations in team practice. It means developing, side-by-side with members of "out-groups," the humane philosophic base upon which common aspects of the ethics of the helping professions are founded.

We have discussed elsewhere some of the skills and attitudes professional education should cultivate to facilitate students' moving into interdisciplinary practice in the ordinary course of their careers. Among the objectives we listed more than a decade ago were. (1) ability to contribute to defining the profession's role as it evolves in various settings, (2) acceptance of the qualifications of colleagues in other disciplines to contribute to such a role definition, (3) understanding the desirability of some overlap of functions as between disciplines, (4) capacity (and willingness) to contribute to the definition of colleagues' responsibilities.

It would certainly seem desirable that every effort be made to provide neophyte professionals a firsthand opportunity to acquire interdisciplinary skills under optimal conditions of practice. Yet graduates of professional schools may find themselves handicapped if their education has failed to prepare them for the contingency of encountering not just the very best, but a diversity of patterns of interdisciplinary collaboration as well. There may be much to be learned even in team practice situations where status-jockeying presents a model of relationships the student need not be encouraged to emulate.

The professional school teaches elements of professional and interprofessional etiquette. But it also endeavors to inculcate the student with the values of the profession, encouraging practice in conformity with the established ethic of the profession. A major concern might therefore be to evolve an indoctrination process that would make it reasonably likely that the graduate's hierarchy of values would be such that he had a higher regard, say, for his responsibilities to clients than for ceremonies of deference on the part of associates from other disciplines.

Teaching the most generic aspect of pertinent skills is a fundamental principle of professional education, since a distinctive characteristic of professional work is the employment of a disciplined judgment in solving a very wide range of *ad hoc* problems. Technique is regarded as inherently subject to improvement, the emphasis in teaching, therefore, is upon approaches found to have been productive of a succession of progressively more valuable techniques. It follows, therefore, that a potentially fruitful orientation to the cultivation of interpersonal relationships may be at least as essential as technical training in specific task performance.

Generically oriented teaching would also approach the division of labor not by providing instruction stipulating particular role expectations as "givens," but rather as the outcome of a problem-solving process; situation defined roles may be viewed as transitory arrangements allocating responsibility and authority — and just possibly any given arrangement may not be the most desirable one.

Such teaching encourages students to examine alternate systems of teamwork, whereas instruction in the intricacies of a single prevailing interdisciplinary setup precludes consideration of even the possibility of a structurally more satisfactory way of arranging the work on hand. Professional students should learn to ask pregnant questions recurrently, so their knowledge is always up to date; mere informational teaching in this area burdens the student with masses of already obsolescing data.

Professional education, if it is to lead to vocational competence, must provide not only for learning in the classroom, but for explorations elsewhere as well. This includes experience in interdisciplinary teamwork alongside learners of different professions. However, to be effective, team practice settings must really afford opportunities for becoming responsibly involved in the tasks and problems of fellow-students; working "alongside" affords small education in and of itself.

It should be noted in this connection that the professional school is not usually itself the operator of the direct-service settings in which its students are afforded opportunities to apply their theoretic learning to practical problems. Those who act as instructors in field programs, therefore, commonly are directly responsible to supervisors concerned with services to clients in the setting, whatever their relationships may be with schoolmen engaged in undiluted academic practice. The complex organization in which the student is learning team practice will have a vested interest in his rendering some measure of productive service while he is a learner there. Its senior personnel will stress the student's achieving an understanding of their particular setting, and of the way or ways teams practice there. Teaching addressed to more general objectives may be accorded little support, and may even seem somewhat subversive of the very specific goals of the particular organization. There is still another loyalty expected of instructors in the field: like all other teachers, they are expected to respond to the needs of their students. And students will frequently be preoccupied with success in their "here and how" practice − success in task performance rather than in learning. The field instructor, if he is to achieve the highest objectives of a truly professional curriculum must be imaginative enough to devise an approach satisfying the needs of the organization, the student and the client, yet responsive to overarching concerns of the profession's future.

If instruction in the field can be called a well-established technique in professional education, as much may be said of instruction based upon typical cases from clinical practice. There is already some employment of records illustrating problems and conflicts in interdisciplinary team practice. But, to the best of our knowledge, a case book specifically addressed to questions of group structure and process, presenting illustrative material from a variety of settings and a large number of professions is not yet available. Such case material as is available at present is freighted with substantive issues of one or another particular discipline, although the more imaginative teachers are moved to bring interdisciplinary team issues into sharp focus.

Our observations on methods of teaching interdisciplinary teamwork would be incomplete without some reference to recent discussions of the characteristics desirable in faculty offering such education. It was the consensus of a group of prominent psychologists in the community mental health field a few years ago that students in their area should be prepared for community work by an "interdisciplinary" faculty, and many suggested that the student body itself should be "interdisciplinary." But "it was generally agreed that the administrative control of training should remain in the hands of psychologists."

Along similar lines, professional identity was stressed by leading medical educators in recommending a senior psychiatrist both as role model and as the essential teacher for residents in community psychiatry. The need they reported, in the same year the psychologists published, was for students' being afforded experience with various types of interprofessional partnerships, to improve understanding of the distinctive contributions diverse collaborators are qualified to make.

To sum up: Objectives of professional education pertinent to interdisciplinary team practice do not appear to be a hotly contended matter among professors in the professional schools, though some educators may accord this area rather lower priority than others. However, little can be definitely regarded as "agreed upon" content, even among those who have endorsed development of this curriculum sector. There is a pressing need for "outcome" studies with reference to the relative utility of various pedagogical techniques or settings employed in teaching about interdisciplinary teamwork. In calling attention to these knowledge gaps, we by no means deny the existence of a body of informed opinion concerning these matters. Informed opinion may ultimately be confirmed as scientifically useful knowledge, but drawing some distinction between the two seems advisable if the planning of professional and interprofessional education is to achieve real maturity.

Conclusion

As interdisciplinary teams come to figure more largely in the part professionals play in the world of work, more attention may be turned to implications teams may have for the history of professionalism as a social movement. We have endeavored in this chapter to formulate some salient questions. To answer most of these will require field studies and empirical testing of even the most apparently sensible propositions. Even around those questions about which some body of background research has already been developed, considerable additional field investigation seems indicated.

One fundamental problem to which it would appear more thought might well be devoted is the nature of expertness. Discussions of professional people and professional work commonly identify some distinctive area of skill and knowledge as crucial. Not uncommonly the implication is that characteristic skill and knowledge is also unique, in a sense a monopoly guarded by the particular occupational group. In interdisciplinary teams, however, it appears that shared understandings and something by way of a comprehensive, synthetic perspective are both desirable and feasible. Considerable inquiry and reflection, however, seem to be indicated before it will be possible to formulate criteria differentiating what can in fact be shared from that sector of the knowledge base which perforce must remain the more private resource of those who are completely initiated. The notion of expertness, as we have demonstrated above, impinges upon role definition, task interrelations, interprofessional communication and collaborative possibilities in the planning of work and its evaluation. Society's need for experts likewise is the fundamental reason for establishing enterprises dedicated to specialized education, preparing both for the several professions and for joint operations.

In considering professionals, professionalism and professionalization, the part played by values, as we have indicated, is a central concern. There has been little published reflection about the impact of team practice upon the distinctive commitments of individual professional workers to "their" clients — commitments which have so fundamentally characterized traditionally structured relationships. A useful purpose would clearly be served by a meticulous compilation and review of some sort of variorum edition of "Professional Ethics: Here and Now." It is clearly insufficient to aver that "professionals" have high ethical standards, without scrutinizing divergent understandings of the way such standards affect interprofessional enterprises. Field studies of deviance from complex organization norms could well be supplemented by some more ample empirical reports of the experience of practitioners, not merely in status contests, but around questions of diverse conceptions of the way a professional goes about serving the public — if he finds himself a member of an interdisciplinary team.

The delicate interrelations among judgment, knowledge and skill have been remarked upon by students of professionalism. But little has been made of the opportunity presented by interdisciplinary team practice to identify explicitly the occasions where the professional person must be willing to risk error or failure. How collegial criticism and surveillance affect willingness to run such hazards, and the extent to which colleagues are candid in acknowledging the limitations of their knowledge base are likewise subjects which are deserving of more intensive inquiry.

The part played by interdisciplinary team relationships in the professionalization of several upwardly mobile occupations has been more noted than actually explored, to date. Reference group theorists have remarked upon the importance to newer occupational groups of norms accepted by high status professions. But the fields of practice where interdisciplinary team staffing patterns are typical have yet to be insightfully reviewed from this perspective.

Little is known, apparently, about the prestige of interdisciplinary teamworkers within their respective professional associations, nor have there been studies of these professionals as special-interest groups. Comparative data on salary status, professional offices and rewards, etc., might contribute materially to elucidating the social situation of the interdisciplinary teamworker. The same may be said of even the simplest inquiries regarding age of entry into interdisciplinary team practice, by practice setting and profession. Some concerted review of characteristic career patterns of interdisciplinary teamworkers is likewise desirable.

The part played by a common ideology in cementing interdisciplinary bonds among mental health workers has been rather amply documented. Comparable studies of interdisciplinary teamwork in public health, corrections and rehabilitation might well push understanding of professionalism, generally, across new frontiers.

The presentation of professionalism and professionalization in interdisciplinary team practice has concluded here with a brief exposition of some considerations in professional education for interdisciplinary team membership, together with some information about typical aspects of certain recent educational proposals in various professions. We have touched upon specific objectives educators might have in mind in curriculum planning, indicating the teaching methods which are involved in attaining those objectives, as well as the content. The topics dealt with included: role models and conceptions of interdisciplinary team practice with which students become familiar and questions about organization analysis, group process and information theory. We have pointed out that learning about interdisciplinary teams will probably be affected by the character of field practice situations afforded students, and the orientation of their instructors in the practice setting. Considerable importance has been attached here to learning about professional subcultures and the crucial significance of sometimes-subtle interprofessional differences in values and criteria of credibility. We have suggested that there may be greater agreement among educators regarding objectives in teaching about interdisciplinary teams than may be the case with content or pedagogical techniques.

If practice in interdisciplinary teams is becoming increasingly important in the professions, it follows that cultivation of team-readiness and relevant aptitudes and skills in learners is a responsibility to which professional schools should be turning their attention. A receptive attitude, a readiness to share, is probably easier for students to achieve; changing the outlook of experienced professionals requires prodigies of energy and a persuasion that absolutely paramount values are in hazard. Conceivably, professional schools may one day include among the personal characteristics looked for in applicants, traits specifically related to educability for team practice. The hope of a more relaxed, more fruitful collaborative ambience emerging seems clearly to depend upon progress along these lines.

Selected References

Amos, Franklyn B.: The manpower predicament of the public health department. Amer J Public Health, 55:1437, 1965.

Bartlett, Harriet M.: Social Work Practice in the Health Field. New York, National Assn. of Social Workers, 1961.

Brayfield, Arthur H.: About special privilege — and special responsibility. Amer Psychol, 20:857, 1965.

Bucher, Rose, and Strauss, Anselm: Professions in process. American J Sociol, 66:325, 1961.

Carr-Saunders, A.M., and Wilson, P.A.: Professions. In Encyclopaedia of the Social Sciences. New York, Macmillan, 1934, vol XII, p. 476.

Carter, Launor F., and Margolin, Joseph B.: Psychologists and social workers. Amer Psychol, 19:359, 1964.

Feldstein, Donald: The para-professional and the community college. Social Work, 14:117, 1969.

Hughes, Everett C.: Professions. Daedalus, 92:655, 1963.

Riessman, Frank, and Popper, Hermine I.: Up From Poverty — New Career Ladders for Nonprofessionals. New York, Harper & Row, 1968.

Shepard, William P., and Roney, J.G.: The teaching of preventive medicine in the United States. Milbank Mem Fund Quart, 42, 1964.

Siegel, Earl, et al.: Role changes within the child health conference. Amer J Public Health, 55:832, 1965.

Wilensky, Harold L.: The professionalization of everyone. American J Sociol, 70, 1964.

Yeager, Wayne, et al.: The mental health worker - a new public health professional. American J Public Health, 52:1625, 1962.

Yolles, Stanley F.: The role of the psychologist in comprehensive mental health centers. Amer Psychol, 21:37, 1966.

Zander, Alvin, et al.: Role Relations in the Mental Health Professions. Ann Arbor, U. of Mich., Inst. for Soc. Res., 1957.

Chapter VII

SUMMARY AND IMPLICATIONS

BECAUSE fairly specific, if tentative, answers to the questions posed in chapters three to six have already been presented as conclusions important in their own right, we shall here only selectively summarize and briefly extend what would appear to be the most promising lines of analysis that might be pursued by practitioners interested in enquiring further into the prospects of interprofessional team practice. We shall discuss first some variables that seem important to consider, then a few somewhat more precise hypotheses and, finally, some observations on recent trends in the field and speculations on the directions of future development.

Variables Commonly Characteristic of Interdisciplinary Teams

The Individual

As we have indicated at the outset, patterns of professional practice are extensively and distinctively affected by individual differences among the practitioners. Occupational roles, however, typically are ill-defined and subject to continual renegotiation.

The individual's conception of his role in the team and of the roles of his colleagues is, of all the variables already explored in field studies, perhaps the most amply documented; its importance seems well established. But what might be summarized as "worker competence" — all the professional skills, attitudes and knowledge that contribute to task performance in the service process — is probably an equally essential variable to consider, in theory and in practice. Another would be the occupationally relevant aspects of personality; we think of this as including initiative, sociability (and, more specifically, volubility) and "style" in work. Personal goals and objectives on the job, attitudes toward clients and toward the work in general, professional ideology and social philosophy might be grouped together in another configuration.* A worker's past is a living force in the present; some of the experience at other times in other places likely to appear as factors in present time include: previous professional experience (in particular, team experience), professional education as it was incorporated by a particular worker, and the plethora of events which cumulate as social class and ethnic background. Latent variables such as the age and the sex of the worker impinge upon the team, age commonly being linked with career stage — yet another variable discussed, along with the above, in chapter six.

We perceive the interrelation of individual worker and team as reciprocal: the team structures the scope of the individual's productive opportunities, and the individual contributes to the pattern and "atmosphere" of team collaborative practice. The activity of each is delimited by the other, just as the activity of each is expedited by the other.

The Team as a Work Group

The way professional activity is organized, the structure and the processes whereby services are provided — both follow distinctive patterns where the work is performed by an interdisciplinary team. Evaluation procedure, internal communications and work flow, for example, are all significantly affected by the closeness of the bond that links together the various specialists who comprise the group.

The team's characteristic approach to its work appears to us to be central to any analysis of the service situation, although it differs materially from team to team. We suggested in chapter four that the extent and nature of task interrelation can be conceptualized by differentiating two types of collaboration: "integrative" and "coordinated." In the former scheme of things, colleagues pool their energies and their expertness, usually combining forces in a multiplicity of joint operations and *ad hoc* consultations. In the latter, each semiautonomous worker

---

*Reference group analysis becomes pertinent in this connection.

undertakes to provide those services requiring his specialized skills; the tasks to be performed by each member are distinctive, if not unique, and the whole group turns its attention to problems only on set occasions, e.g., regularly scheduled case conferences. The extent of consensus on work rules, role definition, the reciprocity of rights and duties as well as the occasions and processes of decision-making, are all variables implicit in the two collaborative styles mentioned above.

This "technological" approach also implies examination of such variables as tempo and scheduling, and the division of labor in organizing the service process into interdependent phases. Channels available for feedback as well as the sharing of information, techniques employed in the "processing" of information to be shared (e.g., recording), and the attitudes of colleagues toward sharing the work constitute still another constellation of production variables. To these we would add team goals (explicit and implicit), and the processes as well as the criteria in evaluating effectiveness and efficiency of both the team and its individual workers.

Reviewing the factors affecting teams' joint approach to the work, we found a gap between the extensive theoretic inquiries into small group behavior and the testing of these generalizations in interdisciplinary team practice settings. The question of applicability is not merely one of empirical testing; we are not sure which of the variables theoretically differentiated by such social scientists as Bales, Bennis, Festinger, Hollander, Likert, Perrow, Ruesch, Scheff and Stogdill will prove pertinent to interdisciplinary team phenomena as actually encountered in the practice field. Leadership, influence, authority, power and status − to mention but a few familiar concepts − are clearly germane to the analysis of interdisciplinary teamwork. The same may be said of decision-making processes and the question of alternation or rotation of workers into a focal position vis-a-vis their colleagues, at one or another phase of a service process, one or another stage in the life of a team.

Team solidarity is a key to understanding the productive operation, and the fate of the group is affected by long-term trends in solidarity. We would relate to this such variables as morale and "atmosphere," cohesion, the history of cliques, and prevalent attitudes toward risk-taking, errors and failure, and the exercise of judgment in the employment of professional knowledge. We alluded to team goals above; the prevailing ideology and the ideological homogeneity of the team might be added as related variables. And solidarity, in turn, may be affected by that aspect of evaluative process which explicitly distinguishes "efficiency" (the amount of effort, perhaps measured in manhours, expended to achieve a specified result) from "effectiveness" (the degree of success attained). We conceive of policy-making processes and policy on policy (discussed in chapter five) as additional variables impinging upon group solidarity.

Finally, there is a group of administrative variables important to consider, such as budgeting and procedure in personnel actions, e.g., hiring, evaluating, promoting, changing salary, firing. Actually, pertinent variables are implicit in answers to the questions: who does what in relation to whom and when? These answers also point to the various ways interdisciplinary teams may be articulated into the complex organizations which constitute their host settings.

Relations with the Complex Organization

As administrative subunits, interdisciplinary teams present distinctive problems to planners and executives in the "host" organization within which they operate — a theme developed early in chapter five. Perhaps the most fundamental forms of assistance central administrations typically provide subsidiary teams are those least discussed in books and articles on interdisciplinary teamwork: funds, plant, maintenance and clerical services, and the multiplicity of supporting departments and services that may be found in a sizeable enterprise (accounting and payroll, personnel, protective services, supplies and purchases, etc.). In addition to these more mundane matters, sponsoring organizations provide interdisciplinary teams varying service in relation to contacts with community agencies or public officials, liaison with professional organizations or accrediting bodies, public relations and publicity.

While scholars have devoted little attention to the above

auxiliary services, the question of complex organization "interference" with interdisciplinary teams has been discussed repeatedly. There can be no questioning the relevance of such variables as the extent of the larger collectivity's bureaucratization, and the manner in which its regulatory and evaluative policy is brought to bear upon the team. The prevailing atmosphere in the agency, moreover, is likely to constitute a significant part of the team's ambience. Organizations in the same field differ, and there is variation, too, among those dedicated to scientific ends and among those which are essentially professional; likewise the business-like agency may afford an interdisciplinary team a work setting significantly different from that provided by a department of government.

We would also attach importance to the nature of the social goals of the dominant organization and the ways in which these figure in the immediate milieu of the team. Efforts of the agency to promote its own specific orientation program for new employees over and above what the team undertakes, likewise must be considered a significant variable when studying an interdisciplinary team in the field. Finally, we would mention the mechanics of liaison and the character of established channels of communication between the complex organization and the team; this would also implicate a parent agency's interest in a team's leader or executive, and the prevailing patterns of influence of each upon the other.

Professionalism and Professionalization

Factors related to the establishing of professional identity are perhaps the more salient ones considered in chapter six, in our discussion of interdisciplinary teams in their relation to professionalism and professionalization. There is, for example, some question as to whether professional skills and characteristics typically are unique or merely distinctive; opinions in this regard vary among workers, among colleagues, among teams, among complex organizations and among the professional associations and their related educational institutions. Professional skills employed (and improved) on the job are of interest also in examining variations of the esteem in which team workers may be held by their professional peers in other work settings. The identity issue is also clearly a material consideration in role negotiation (which tasks, for example, are appropriately performed by which professional) and in the professionalization process (what performance achievements or work relationships, for example, distinguish the member of a profession from a subprofessional or technical worker). The nature of professional expertness becomes a consideration in determining who may evaluate whom, and in defining a crucial shadow zone in practice where certainty is minimal and professional knowledge is only sufficient to provide a foundation for professional judgment. Of course, in the work situation observable criteria besides these serve to identify the professional. Certification-accreditation procedures consequently become matters of concern to interdisciplinary teams; the same may be said of the content of professional education in pertinent fields.

Another strategic variable in assessing the impact of professionalism is systems of value, for the extent of consensus about team goals in some wise reflects what individual workers have come to believe is important about their own contributions. Diverse conceptions of "the" professional relationship, also, are rooted in the ethical codes of the different professions. The very content of professional work in the team setting is determined in large part by attitudes workers may be most reluctant to modify, and by reference groups whose expectations have been quite explicitly defined. Opinions, for example, differ regarding the relative importance to be attached to individual (client) as contraposed to social (community) interest, in the event the two conflict.

Among the many variables we have touched upon in the preceding overview, a few in each area seem especially strategic both in theory and in practice. Each of these variables may figure as one of the determinants of team effectiveness, or as a catalytic agent affecting the extent of influence exerted by some other factor.

Within the team itself, the nature of any previous interdisciplinary experience on the part of individuals has much to do with such workers' attitudes and expectations; consequently, morale and probably the productivity of the group are involved. The clarity of role and status definition and the measure of consensus in this regard, are material considerations in determining the coherence of the team's endeavor to render professional service. Prevailing patterns of leadership and authority vary from team to team and are, of course, related to developments in each team's approach to questions of role and status; the processes whereby workers influence one another, and the whole area of decision-making – both clinical and administrative – may be viewed as leadership phenomena. Teams differ in their handling of the problem of "organizational socialization," but the way workers are helped to find their way into the group affects team solidarity and has an important bearing upon a team's long-range prospects for continuity and survival. All these considerations were developed at some length in the third chapter.

Since we suggest that collaborative practice in the interdisciplinary team constitutes a new development in the history of professionalism, it follows that different approaches to working in collaboration are of importance. We believe that the suggested distinction between an integrated and a coordinated approach is worth exploring because of its relationship both to productivity problems and to the dilemma of insularity among specialists. Diverse approaches to the division of labor doubtless are associated with the unfolding of one or another type of developmental pattern in the "natural history" of teams. The nature of this relationship remains relatively obscure, as the historical approach has rarely been employed in studies of interdisciplinary teams. It would appear, however, that there may be a multiple-causation pattern linking the approach to collaboration and specified characteristics of individual workers comprising a team; the two factors jointly affect the likelihood of continuing group effectiveness. In chapter four, these considerations were explored in greater detail.

Among the determinants of the team's relationship with its host agency, the most pervasive and, probably, the most influential is the extent of that organization's bureaucratization. Among the determinants of the effectiveness of an interdisciplinary group's work, two considerations loom large: the character of the team's responsibility to outside authority, and the extent to which it is constrained in identifying its own work problems and endeavoring to cope with them. Rigid rules and bureaucratic approaches in applying them raise problems for the traditionally oriented professional person; it remains to be ascertained just how much team process is affected by such systems. A more extended development of this theme is found in chapter five.

Finally, we believe that the attitudes of professional associations and of professional schools create a very important part of the work atmosphere of interdisciplinary teams, and that the expectations of community groups as well as clients, affect teams' definitions of goals as well as their day-to-day performance. The activity of a team cannot be understood solely as a function of the aspirations and the skills of the associated practitioners; nor does the ambience provided by a host agency fill out the picture. The team's milieu is the larger society, and the expectations to which it responds impinge upon it from many different quarters. This particular aspect of the social situation of the interdisciplinary team is discussed in chapter six.

In highlighting a few strategic variables, we do not mean to suggest either that these are the only important dimensions to be studied or that these few are representative of all important categories of variables. It is our contention, however, that no study of an interdisciplinary team can hope to present even a moderately comprehensive picture if there are no observations in these areas. And, conversely, we believe that a vigorous and imaginative exploration of these key aspects alone is likely to result in a team portrait that is at once dynamic and substantial.

Some Additional Hypotheses

The variables presented at the beginning of this chapter were arranged with reference to the four perspectives developed in the body of the discussion. We present at this point some final hypotheses interrelating the various perspectives. These hypothesized relationships include ideas we believe may prove important to practice strategies and the preparation of tomorrow's team operations. They are intended as illustrations only; a listing of all possibly fruitful research themes would be patently impracticable.

Team Effectiveness

The contribution "strong" leadership can make to effectiveness will depend upon members' willingness, in principle, to accept leadership in the practice situation. (See Chapter III.)

Teams which have explicit plans for the deployment of identified expertness in workers are more effective than those in which work is not planned in this way. (See Chapters III and IV.)

Team effectiveness is enhanced to the extent that intrateam communication channels enhance feedback. (See Chapter IV.)

Effective teams make decisions not according to bureaucratic rules, but in conformity with the best (independent) judgment of professionals. (See Chapter V.)

In preparing students for interdisciplinary team practice, schools in certain professions have had greater success (as one can tell from the conduct of graduates) than schools in other professions. Why has professional education met the challenge more adequately in some fields than in others? Within a single field, what explains the differences in achievement among the various schools? (See Chapter VI.)

Team Solidarity

Efforts to induce organizational socialization through the team will be more successful than efforts to cultivate staff attachments to the host agency. (See Chapter III.)

Under what circumstances does intragroup conflict result not in chaos, but in an enhancement of solidarity? (See Chapter III.)

Group cohesion not built upon a reconciliation of diverse professional values will prove unsatisfactory by the pragmatic test of productive activity, regardless of any essentially friendly relations among colleagues. (See Chapters III and IV.)

Where the complex organization appears to intercede in the team's affairs capriciously, solidarity is impaired. (See Chapters IV and V.)

Relationships with Clients

Success in work may be difficult to assess because the team, or some practitioner, may be trying to provide clients with a particular type of service where the clients express a need for something quite different. (See Chapters III and V.)

Client attitudes toward the team, its members and its services reflect workers' attitudes toward the team — hostility toward a team leader, for example. (See Chapter V.)

Alternatively Satisfactory Arrangements

If a team includes several workers who are each secure in their own expertness and willing to share work and initiatives with workers in other disciplines, the division of labor may be arranged quite amiably. (See Chapters III and IV.)

But of two teams, each characterized by an amiable arrangement of duties and responsibilities, working conditions in one may be more conducive to risk-taking and the exercise of ingenuity. (See Chapters III and IV.)

If a team includes a worker in a high-status profession who aspires to lead and a number of other workers who regard their own professions as ancillary to his, the division of labor may be arranged quite amiably. (See Chapters III and V.)

Which ways of organizing the work ensure maximum employment of the highest skills of each team member? (See Chapters III and VI.)

Team Response to Crises

In teams where final decisions are made by a leader, any project about which any worker expresses strong doubts will be aborted in the leader's absence. (See Chapter III.)

In teams where integrated work patterns prevail, the group will pool marginal skills in a crisis to cover a gap left by a worker who is ill, or a position unfilled. (See Chapters IV and VI.)

Ideologically homogeneous teams will react with vigor on professional rather than personal grounds to ideologically threatening policy decisions of host agency. (See Chapter V.)

Recent Trends and
Directions of Future Development

Manpower planners concerned with developing more amply staffed services in the helping and healing fields are by no means unanimously agreed upon the desirability of continued efforts to break work down into an increasing number of specialities. Both community psychiatry and public health are testing new occupational titles reflecting a "generalist" approach, and there have been those in the rehabilitation field who question the impact of recurrent consultation upon organizational efficiency.

The main current, nonetheless, has been in the direction of continued division of labor as an expedient to achieving the most economical employment of the skills of top professionals.* Dr. Philip R. Lee, who headed the twelve billion-dollar-a-year federal health program under President Johnson, has estimated that at least one hundred thousand new health workers a year will be needed in the nineteen seventies, yet medical schools today graduate only about eight thousand physicians. If the deficit is to be made up, the likelihood is that a new army of "medical therapists" or "assistant physicians" will have to be trained in curricula which at this writing are, largely, yet to be devised. A beginning has been made at rethinking the tasks assigned to various practitioners of the healing arts, yet Dr. Earle Marsh, who heads the nation's first Health Professions Council (in San Francisco) has declared that as a surgeon he spends only a third of his time operating, while the average nurse puts in only a quarter of her time at patients' bedsides. Most professionals, as we pointed out earlier, work at (or close to) their highest level of skill only a small part of the time, but a careful analysis of their activities (especially time spent at quasi-clerical tasks) could point the way to a more rational employment of labor and more efficient approaches to teamwork. An example has been set by community

---

*The development of collaborative practice in grade and high schools, involving teams of master teachers, assistants, aides and clerks has scarcely begun.

mental health centers in a few of the many cities where they have been established: ' mental health aides" in Rochester, New York, work under the supervision of psychiatric social workers, facilitating referrals, organizing parent groups, etc.; and of 262 employees at the center operated by Lincoln Hospital in the South Bronx (New York City), 140 are nonprofessionals, including technical aides and community workers from the neighborhood, specially recruited and trained to help professional school graduates.

Since specialization in the professions has proceeded farthest, perhaps, in medicine, it is not surprising that team approaches have proliferated not only in hospitals but in a host of paramedical settings as well. For a number of years, assessment of the severity of handicap experienced by persons applying for federally funded aid to the disabled has been the responsibility of multidisciplinary diagnostic teams, including specialists qualified in various branches of medicine and others expert in evaluating impact upon social functioning. Calculations of risk and hazard in paroling prisoners may likewise involve a concert of disciplines. As new techniques and innovative practices are "phased in," *ad hoc* groups or formally established boards control the flow of limited resources; it is no mean task to decide who may benefit by a heart transplant and who is to be denied. And across the country, colleagues sit around the table debating both the criteria for determining which patients have prior right to artificial kidney machines and just how those criteria are to be applied, case by case.*

It is not possible in this study to do any more than suggest the new fields of humane service in which there is a strong likelihood of team collaboration among workers in occupations hardly identifiable at this time. New careers for the poor may bring a new army of paraprofessionals. There is undoubtedly a growing trend toward recruitment of indigenous personnel from among populations reached by governmental and philanthropically funded service programs. This makes for a further diversification

---

*While such decisions may be made by individuals in a position of authority, the peace of mind of patients, relatives, potential patients and hospital personnel may all be best served by a procedure that involves a number of people, a number of points of view, a number of disciplines.

of background (socioeconomically, culturally and in terms of formal education) between staff elements traditionally involved in collaborative endeavor and a sizeable proportion of the newcomers. Furthermore, the prospect is that team process in the future will increasingly have to take into account not only the diverse professional organizations with which workers are affiliated, but their trade union affiliations as well.*

Some of the older generation of professionals have had to learn that there is more than one viable approach to interdisciplinary team practice. Some of the new generation will have to improvise new ways of working with colleagues who lay no claim to professional title, yet have an indispensable contribution to make to the common goal of service to man.

Our own endeavor here has been to delineate some key questions which, it is clear, must be resolved before a more ample understanding of interdisciplinary teamwork can be achieved. Many sensible ideas about joint operations still have to be subjected to scientific test if we are to improve the services to humanity to which those with a vocation to helping and healing are committed. In addition to the problem areas which have tended to preoccupy researchers in this field to date, we therefore reiterate in closing, several themes mentioned in the first part of chapter two. These are the broad questions of social policy and social planning. Is the public interest best served by increasing the proportion of all professional services provided by practitioners engaged in collaborative practice in interdisciplinary teams? What share of the national product ought, appropriately, to be allocated for interdisciplinary team services? What, precisely, should the community expect of workers in the helping-healing professions? What priority should be assigned to integrated services? How is

---

*Yet another cross-current is implicit in the charge (published March 14, 1969 in the San Francisco Chronicle) that well over a hundred nurses in a hospital turned from their professional association to a union of white clerical workers, in their attempt to head off the organizing efforts of another union which had signed up numbers of black orderlies, etc. Contention about racism and alleged racism is likely to be very much a part of the scene for the next decade or more, as deprived ethnic groups (blacks, Mexican-Americans, Indians) move into vocations from which they have, for a variety of reasons, been excluded, and move on up the career ladder. The problems are common to a number of fields; nursing has made rather more progress than many.

"need" to be defined, and who is appropriately to be identified as belonging in the "client" class? How much importance should be attached to preventive rather than therapeutic approaches? These seem to us some of the fundamental issues to which forward-looking practitioners must turn increasing attention.

INDEX

Turnover, 46, 90, 99

U

Unions, 159
Universities & professional schools, 101,
126, 135, 136ff

V

Variables, 147ff

W

Wiener, Daniel, 87

Wilensky, Harold, 146
Wilson, P.A., 146
Work flow, 57, 65ff, 80
"Working with" versus "doing for", 10, 75

Y

Yeager, Wayne, 113, 146
Yolles, Stanley, 130, 146

Z

Zander, Alvin, 146

361
H789t

120 144